250 IQ Brain-teasers

Compiled by

Joe Cameron

JAICO PUBLISHING HOUSE

Ahmedabad Bangalore Bhopal Chennai
Delhi Hyderabad Kolkata Mumbai

Published by Jaico Publishing House
121 Mahatma Gandhi Road
Mumbai - 400 001
jaicopub@vsnl.com
www.jaicobooks.com

© Arcturus Publishing Limited

Published in arrangement with
Arcturus Publishing Limited
1-7 Shand Street, London SE1 2ES

250 IQ BRAIN-TEASERS
ISBN 978-81-7992-842-4

First Jaico Impression: 2006

Printed by SP Printers, E-120, Sector-7, Noida-201301

250 IQ
Brain-teasers

Welcome to *250 IQ Brain-teasers*, a collection of over 250 logic puzzles, mind-benders and mathematical teasers to exercise, occupy and defy your mental abilities.

The book has been carefully compiled into ten levels of ascending difficulty, with the first chapters being easier than the last. The best place to start is at the beginning, with level one, and if you work methodically through the earlier chapters, you should be able to spot the patterns and flow of logic to help with some of the later chapters.

If you become stuck on a particular puzzle, it might be best to move on and come back to it later – always resisting the temptation to flick through to the answer page to put you out of your misery. Often, if you look at the puzzle from a different perspective, then the solution becomes apparent – it's all a question of logic.

250 IQ Brain-teasers is not just about getting the right answer – it's about sharpening your wits and training your mind to think logically. If you get an answer wrong, then look back over the puzzle to see how the solution was arrived at.

On the next page are several tables, which you may find useful. All the puzzles can be solved using standard mathematical or alphabetical calculations, so no other general knowledge is required.

Good luck and enjoy the *250 IQ Brain-teasers*!

Multiplication Table

×	1	2	3	4	5	6	7	8	9	10	11	12
1	1	2	3	4	5	6	7	8	9	10	11	12
2	2	4	6	8	10	12	14	16	18	20	22	24
3	3	6	9	12	15	18	21	24	27	30	33	36
4	4	8	12	16	20	24	28	32	36	40	44	48
5	5	10	15	20	25	30	35	40	45	50	55	60
6	6	12	18	24	30	36	42	48	54	60	66	72
7	7	14	21	28	35	42	49	56	63	70	77	84
8	8	16	24	32	40	48	56	64	72	80	88	96
9	9	18	27	36	45	54	63	72	81	90	99	108
10	10	20	30	40	50	60	70	80	90	100	110	120
11	11	22	33	44	55	66	77	88	99	110	121	132
12	12	24	36	48	60	72	84	96	108	120	132	144

Cube Numbers		Square Numbers		Numerical Values			Prime Numbers
1	1	1		1	A	26	2
2	8	4		2	B	25	
3	27	9		3	C	24	3
4	64	16		4	D	23	
5	125	25		5	E	22	
6	216	36		6	F	21	5
7	343	49		7	G	20	
8	512	64		8	H	19	
9	729	81		9	I	18	7
10	1000	100		10	J	17	
11	1331	121		11	K	16	
12	1728	144		12	L	15	11
13	2197	169		13	M	14	
14	2744	196		14	N	13	13
15	3375	225		15	O	12	
16	4096	256		16	P	11	
17	4913	289		17	Q	10	17
18	5832	324		18	R	9	
19	6859	361		19	S	8	19
20	8000	400		20	T	7	
				21	U	6	
				22	V	5	23
				23	W	4	
				24	X	3	
				25	Y	2	29
				26	Z	1	

PUZZLE 1

What number is missing?

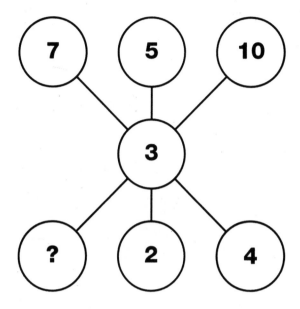

PUZZLE 2

Which number completes the puzzle?

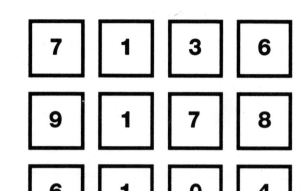

PUZZLE 3

Which number completes this sequence?

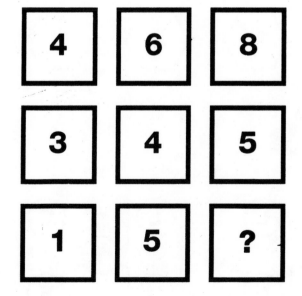

PUZZLE 4

Following a logical sequence, can you complete this puzzle?

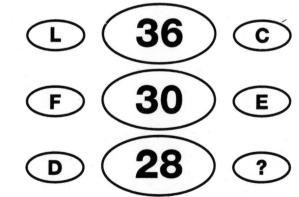

5
PUZZLE

Following a logical sequence, which number needs to be added to complete the puzzle?

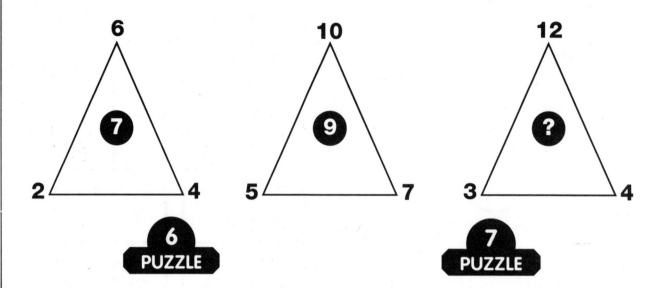

6
PUZZLE

What number is missing?

7
PUZZLE

Which number completes the puzzle?

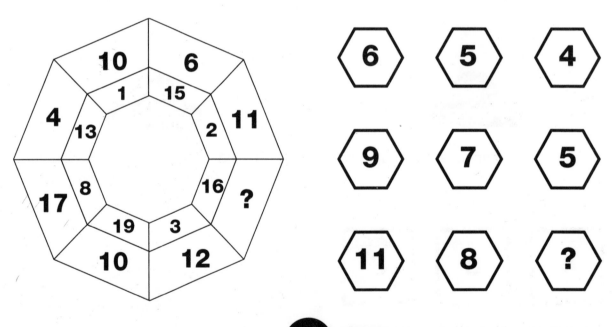

8
PUZZLE

Which letter completes this sequence?

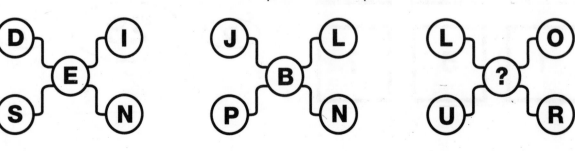

What number is missing?

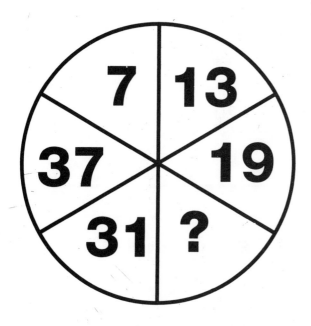

Which letter completes the puzzle?

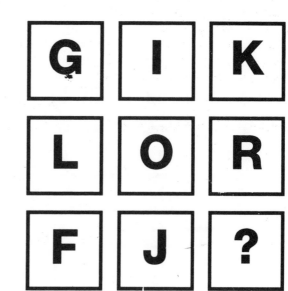

Which number completes this sequence?

Following a logical sequence, can you complete this puzzle?

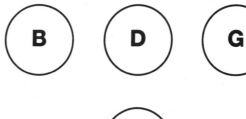

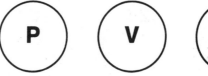

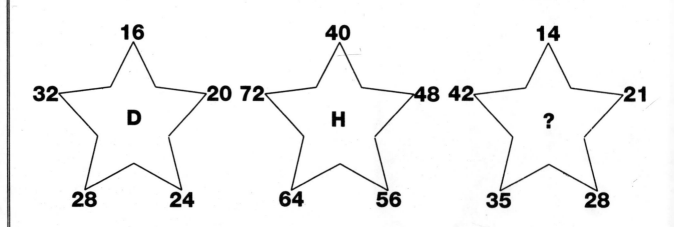

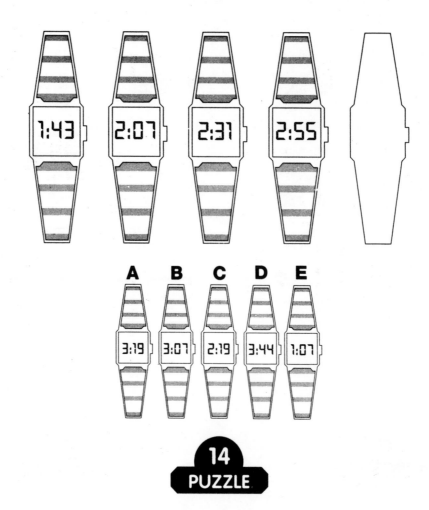

Which watch completes the sequence?

A **B** **C** **D** **E**

Which letter is missing from the last star to
make this puzzle complete?

15 PUZZLE

Which number completes this sequence?

 4   6   3

 7   11   5

13 21 ?

16 PUZZLE

Which number completes this sequence?

5 8 14 26 ?

17 PUZZLE

Which letter needs to be added to continue the sequence?

E H L Q ?

18 PUZZLE

What number needs to be added to the last triangle to complete the puzzle?

3

6

10

15

21

?

19 PUZZLE

Which number should be added to complete the sequence?

25

36

49

64

?

LEVEL

1

PUZZLE 20

Which pattern completes the line?

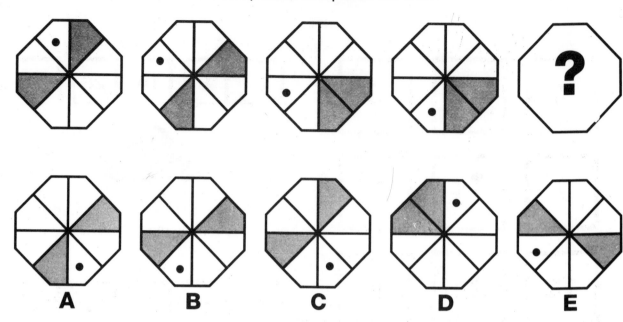

PUZZLE 21

Which of the lower six patterns completes the puzzle?

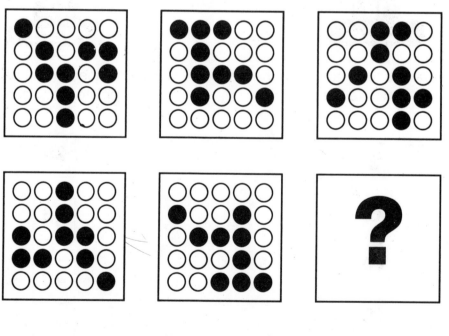

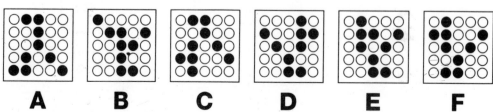

Which playing card goes in the empty space?

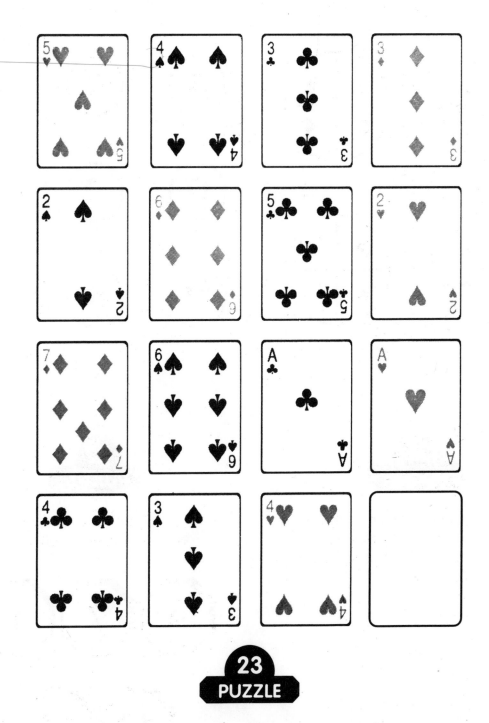

Which number completes the puzzle?

5   6   8

7   8   9   7   9   10

2   3   1   ?

L E V E L

1

15

24 PUZZLE

What is missing from the last circle?

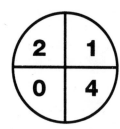

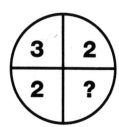

25 PUZZLE

Which letter completes the puzzle?

26 PUZZLE

This arrangement of 8 coins produces a square, with 3 coins per side, can you move 4 of the coins to give a square with 4 coins per side?

27 PUZZLE

Which number replaces the question mark and completes the puzzle?

16

What is the missing arrangement?

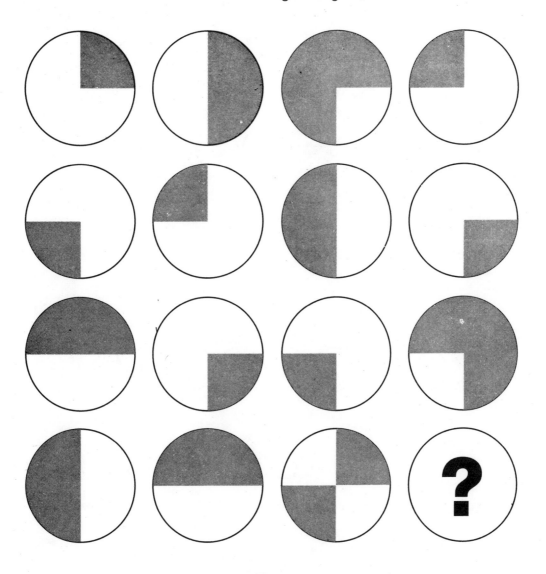

Which domino completes the puzzle?

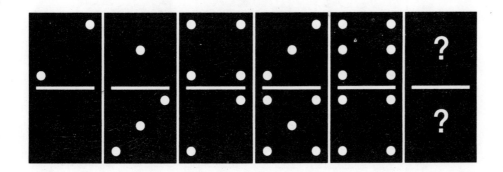

LEVEL

①

PUZZLE 1

Which number goes in the empty circle?

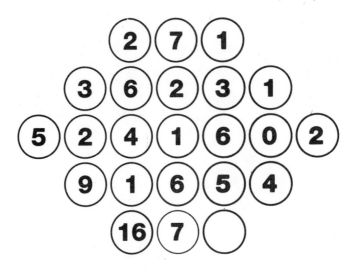

PUZZLE 2

Which of the smaller boxes follows the same rule as these six?

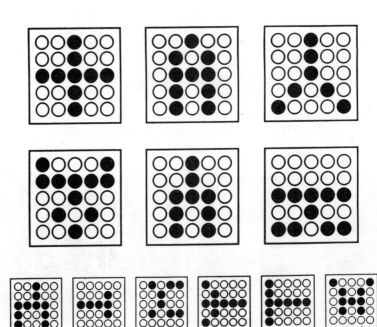

A   B   C   D   E   F

PUZZLE 3

Where does the missing hand go?

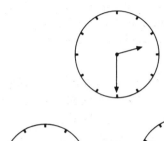

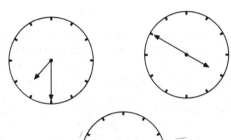

PUZZLE 4

What is missing from the last circle?

 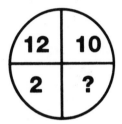

PUZZLE 5

Which letter completes the puzzle?

L   P   V

R   J   B

X   D   ?

PUZZLE 6

Which number completes the puzzle?

2   5   5

4   7   9

6   8   ?

LEVEL

2

19

PUZZLE 7

What is missing from the last star?

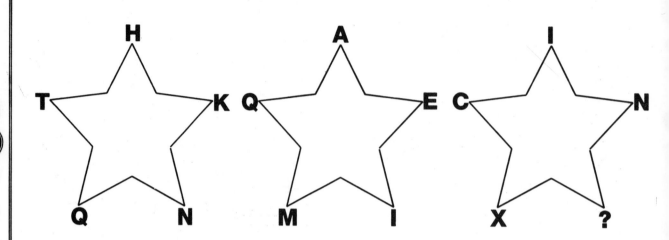

PUZZLE 8

What completes the last triangle?

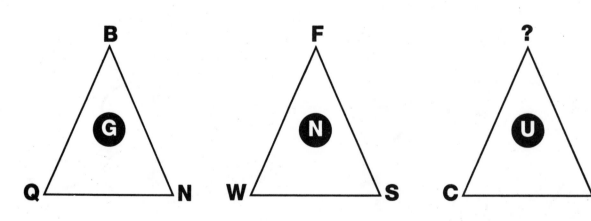

PUZZLE 9

Which letter goes in the lower right hand square to complete the puzzle?

B K E

G M E

I X ?

PUZZLE 10

Which number completes the puzzle?

5 11 6

3

8 14 ?

PUZZLE 11

In this circle which letter goes in the empty segment?

PUZZLE 12

What number fits in this triangle to complete the puzzle?

4

3 5

2 ?

6 5 1 3

LEVEL

2

21

13 PUZZLE

Which number goes in the bottom square to complete the sequence?

2

6

14

30

?

14 PUZZLE

Which number replaces the question mark and completes the puzzle?

7	9	11
6	3	4
4	5	?

15 PUZZLE

Which watch will complete the sequence?

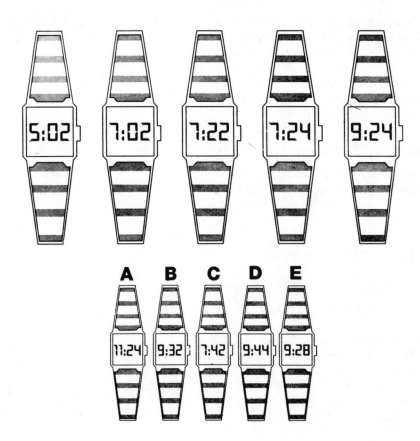

5:02   7:02   7:22   7:24   9:24

A   B   C   D   E
11:24   9:32   7:42   9:44   9:28

Which pattern completes the puzzle?

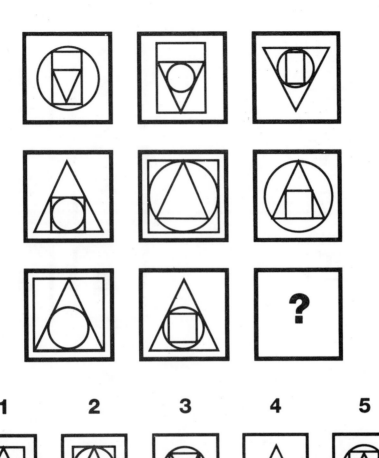

What is missing from the last grid?

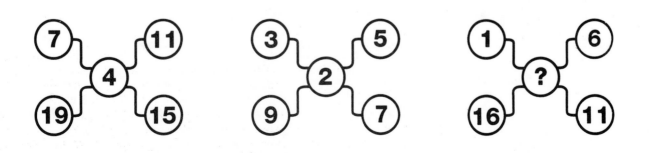

LEVEL

● 2

24

PUZZLE 18

In this sequence of letters what needs to be added to make the puzzle correct?

P	N
T	R
X	V
B	Z
F	D
J	?

PUZZLE 19

Which number replaces the question mark and completes the puzzle?

12	15	18
20	24	28
30	35	?

PUZZLE 20

Which number completes this sequence?

| 21 | 28 | 35 | 42 | ? |

PUZZLE 21

What number goes in the bottom right circle?

2   0   9

23

1   8   ?

What is missing from the last triangle?

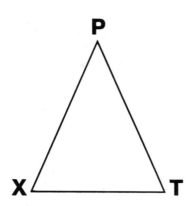
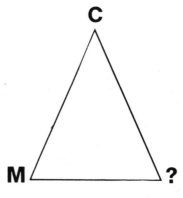

Where does the missing hand go?

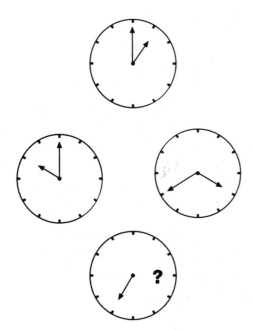

Which letter replaces the question mark and completes the puzzle?

25 PUZZLE

Which number completes this sequence?

26 PUZZLE

What is missing from this circle?

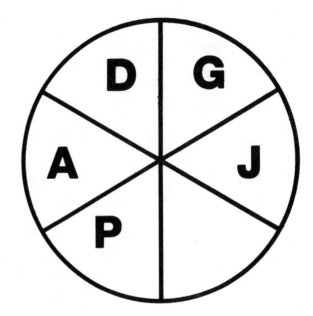

27 PUZZLE

Can you move just 2 matches to create 7 squares?

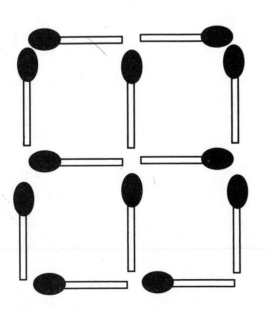

28 PUZZLE

What is missing from this pyramid of numbers?

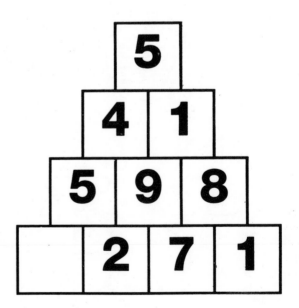

What time should be displayed on the bottom clockface?

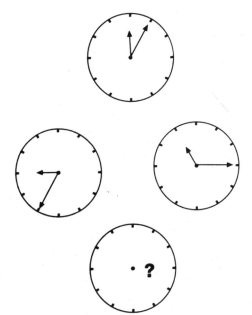

Which four letters complete this puzzle?

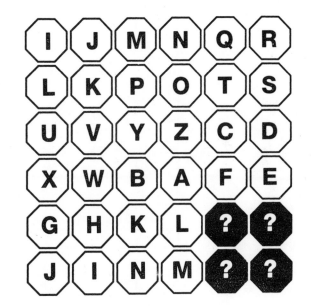

What should be added to the bottom right circle to complete the puzzle?

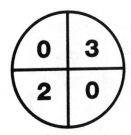 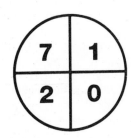 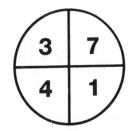

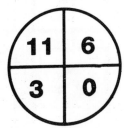 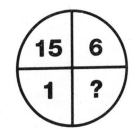

LEVEL

3

PUZZLE 4

What completes this sequence?

3

4

7

11

?

PUZZLE 5

Which number completes this pyramid?

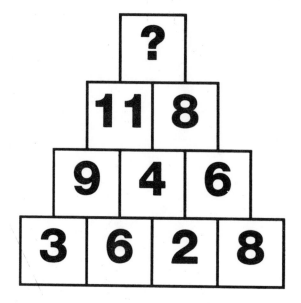

PUZZLE 6

What number is missing from the bottom right circle?

PUZZLE 7

Which number replaces the question mark and completes the puzzle?

2   9   7

5   7   2

6   7   ?

8 PUZZLE

Which of the bottom six grids completes this pattern?

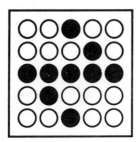
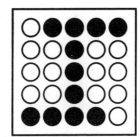
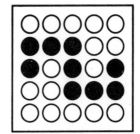

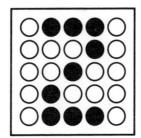

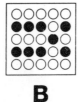

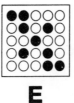
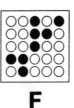

A   B   C   D   E   F

9 PUZZLE

What is missing from the last shape?

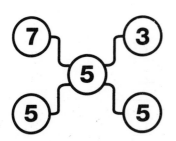
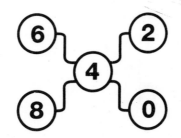
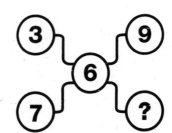

LEVEL

3

30

10 PUZZLE

Which number completes the last triangle?

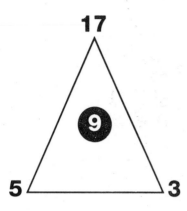

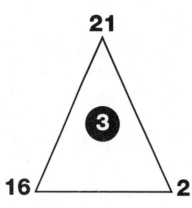

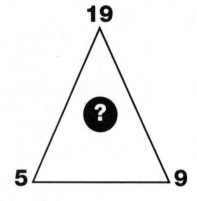

11 PUZZLE

Which number replaces the question mark and completes the puzzle?

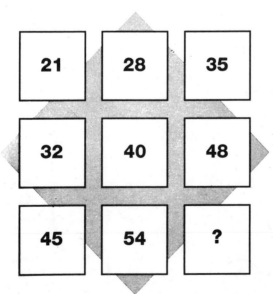

12 PUZZLE

Which number completes this sequence?

0	9
1	6
2	5
3	6
4	9
6	?

PUZZLE 13

What is missing from this circle?

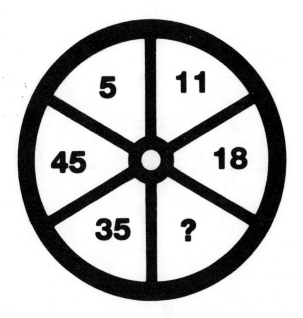

PUZZLE 14

What completes this pattern?

PUZZLE 15

Which number replaces the question mark and completes the puzzle?

10	11	5
4	6	9
3	0	?

PUZZLE 16

What is needed to make this triangle complete?

7

5   2

6   9

3   3   4   ?

LEVEL

● ● ③ ○ ○ ○ ○ ○ ○ ○ ○ ○ ○ ○ ○ ○ ○ ○ ○ ○

PUZZLE 17

Which number is missing?

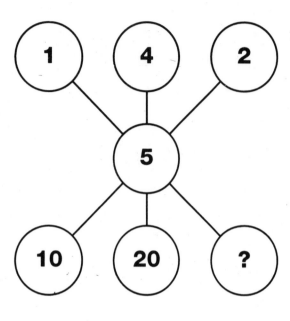

PUZZLE 18

Following a logical sequence, can you complete this puzzle?

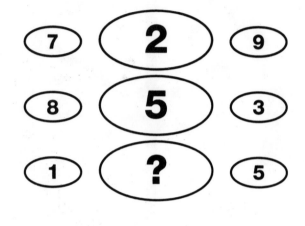

PUZZLE 19

What is needed to complete this pyramid?

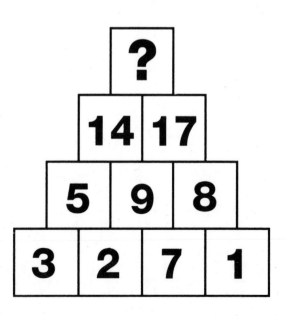

PUZZLE 20

Which number continues the sequence?

| 27 | 64 | 125 | 216 | ? |

PUZZLE 21

Which of the bottom six grids fills the missing gap?

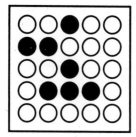 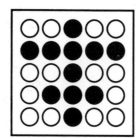 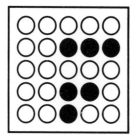

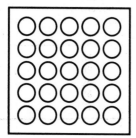 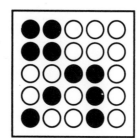 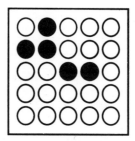

A   **B**   **C**   **D**   **E**   **F**

PUZZLE 22

Following a logical sequence, can you complete this puzzle?

3   6   12   15   21   24   30   33   39   42   48   51   ?

LEVEL 3

33

23 PUZZLE

Which playing cards fill the blank spaces?

PUZZLE 24

Which number is missing?

| 3 | 5 | 7 | 11 | ? |

PUZZLE 25

Here are 5 matches, which form 2 equilateral triangles, can you add 1 match, and move two others, to form 8 equilateral triangles?

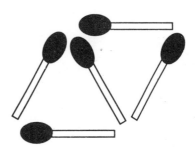

PUZZLE 26

Which letters are the odd ones out?

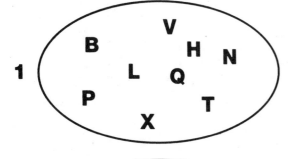

1

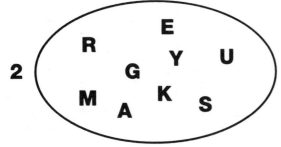

2

PUZZLE 27

Which number completes this circle?

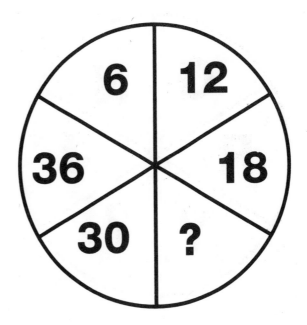

PUZZLE 1

Which letter completes the puzzle?

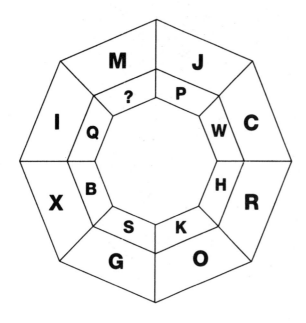

PUZZLE 2

Which **number is missing?**

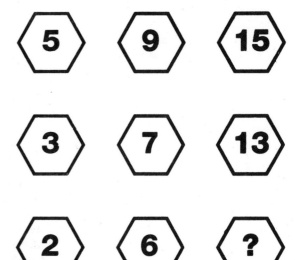

PUZZLE 3

Which letter is needed to complete this circle?

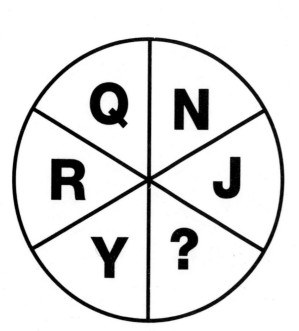

PUZZLE 4

Following a logical sequence, can you complete this puzzle?

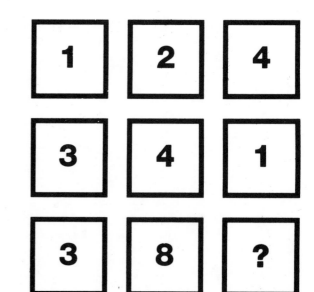

5 PUZZLE

Which of the bottom six grids completes the puzzle?

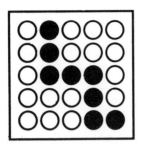 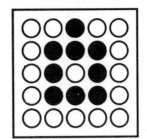 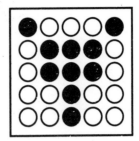

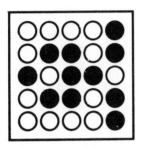 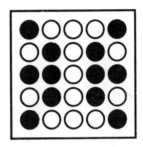  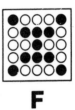

 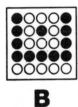 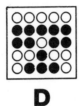 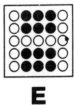

A   **B**   **C**   **D**   **E**   **F**

6 PUZZLE

What time should the last watch show?

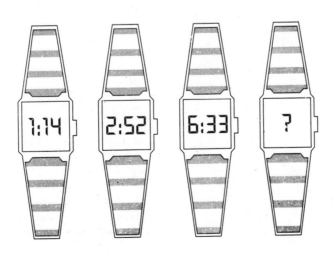

L
E
V
E
L

4

PUZZLE 7

What is missing from the empty circle?

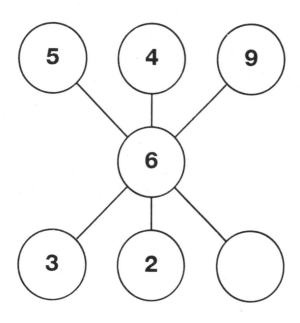

PUZZLE 8

What letter is missing?

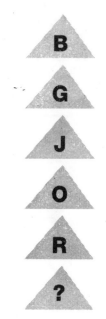

PUZZLE 9

What is missing from the empty segment?

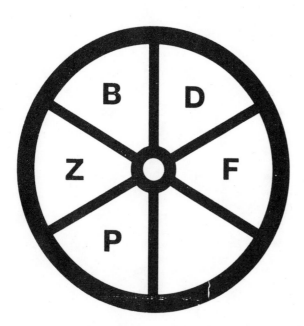

PUZZLE 10

Which letter completes the puzzle?

Following a logical sequence, can you
complete this puzzle?

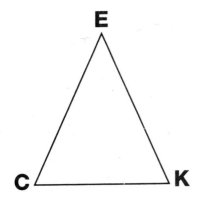

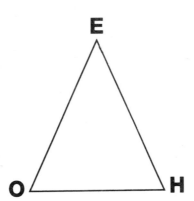

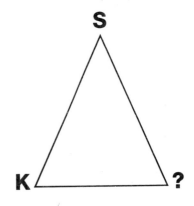

Which three numbers are missing from this pattern?

1	6	2	0	2	4	2	8
2	0	2	**?**	3	0	3	5
2	4	3	0	3	6	4	2
2	8	3	5	4	**?**	4	9
3	2	4	0	4	8	5	6
3	6	4	5	5	4	6	**?**

13 PUZZLE

What number is missing?

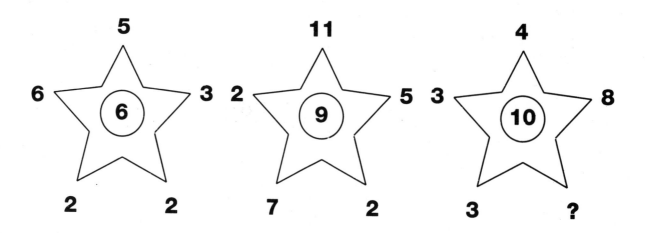

5
6   6   3
2   2

11
2   9   5
7   2

4
3   10   8
3   ?

14 PUZZLE

Which letter is missing?

15 PUZZLE

Following a logical sequence, can you complete this puzzle?

D C H
B G F
I E ?

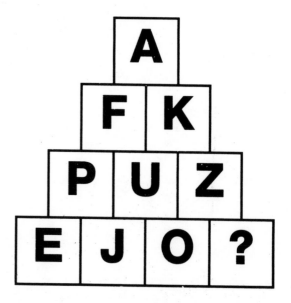

A
F K
P U Z
E J O ?

What is missing from the last segment?

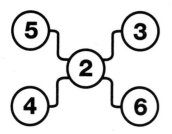 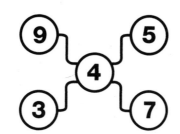 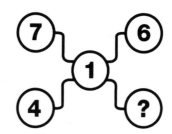

Which number is missing?

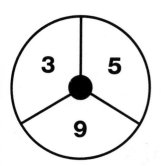 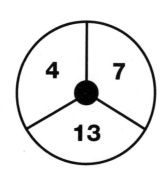 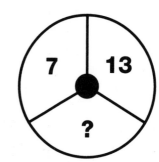

Which letter completes the puzzle?

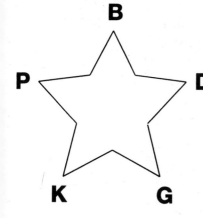 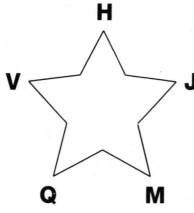 

19 PUZZLE

What completes this sequence?

B   J   E

E   N   J

H   ?   O

20 PUZZLE

Can you move just 3 coins to make the triangle point upwards?

21 PUZZLE

Which number is missing?

3   5   7

11

13   17   ?

22 PUZZLE

Which number is the odd one out in each shape?

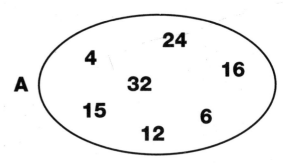

A
24
4
16
32
15
6
12

B
25
9
4
17
15
35

PUZZLE 23

What number is missing?

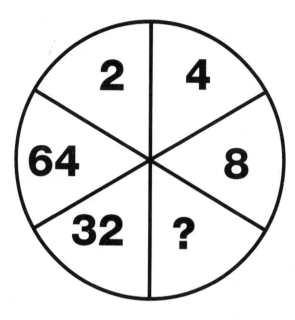

PUZZLE 24

Which letter completes the puzzle?

PUZZLE 25

Following a logical sequence, can you complete this puzzle?

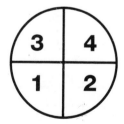 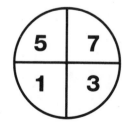

 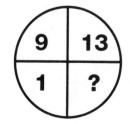

PUZZLE 26

What is missing from the bottom scale to make it balance?

LEVEL
4

PUZZLE 27

Where does the missing hand go?

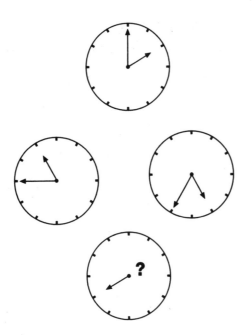

PUZZLE 28

What letter is missing?

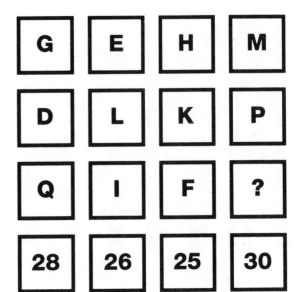

G	E	H	M
D	L	K	P
Q	I	F	?
28	26	25	30

PUZZLE 29

Which piece fits back into the grid to complete the pattern?

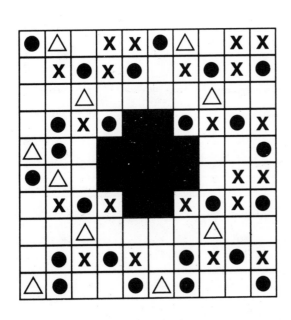

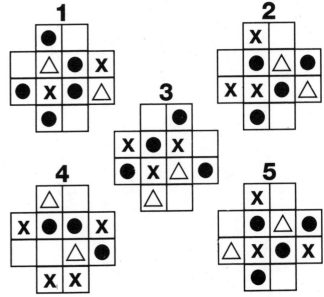

Which number is missing?

Which letter replaces the question mark?

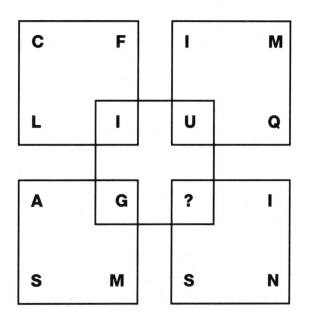

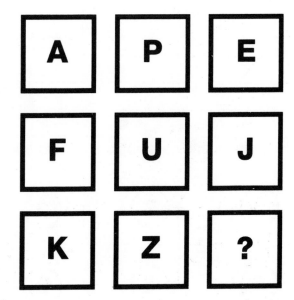

Following a logical sequence, can you complete this puzzle?

Which letter completes the puzzle?

LEVEL 5

5
PUZZLE

Which playing card will complete the puzzle?

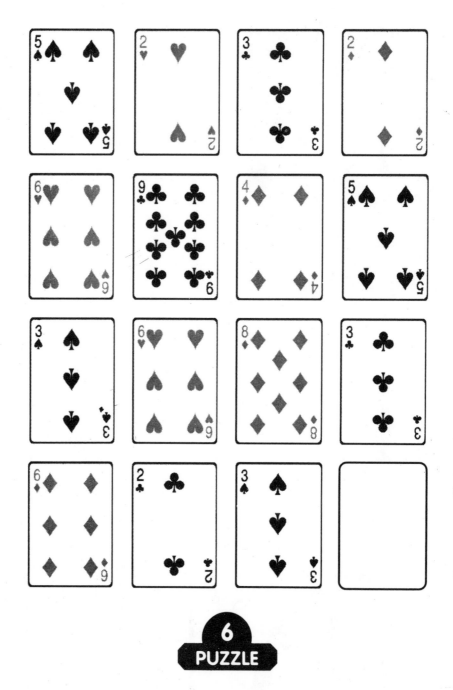

6
PUZZLE

In this sequence of numbers what should go within the last shape to make it complete?

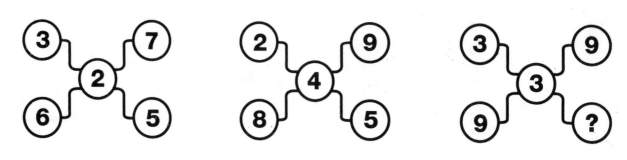

7 PUZZLE

What number is missing?

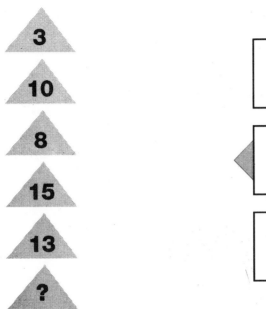

3
10
8
15
13
?

8 PUZZLE

Which letter completes the puzzle?

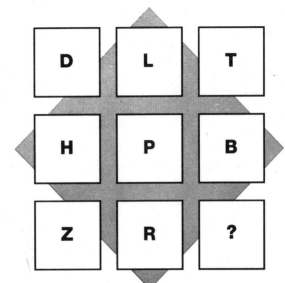

D	L	T
H	P	B
Z	R	?

9 PUZZLE

Which watch should go in the missing space to complete the sequence?

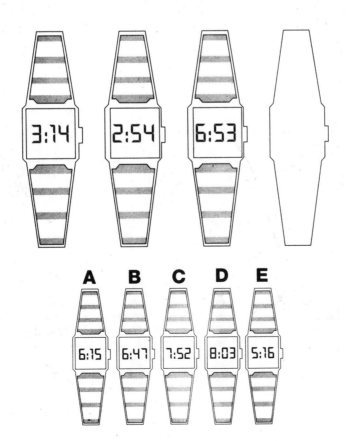

3:14   2:54   6:53

A 6:15   B 6:47   C 7:52   D 8:03   E 5:16

10 PUZZLE

Which number is missing?

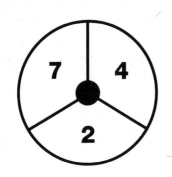

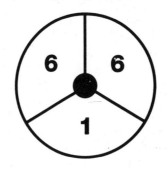

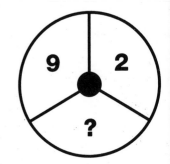

11 PUZZLE

Which of the bottom six grids completes
the puzzle?

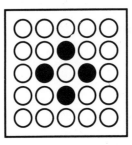

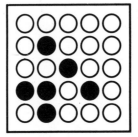

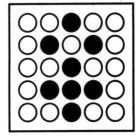

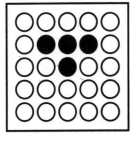

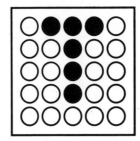

A B C D E F

12 PUZZLE

What number is missing?

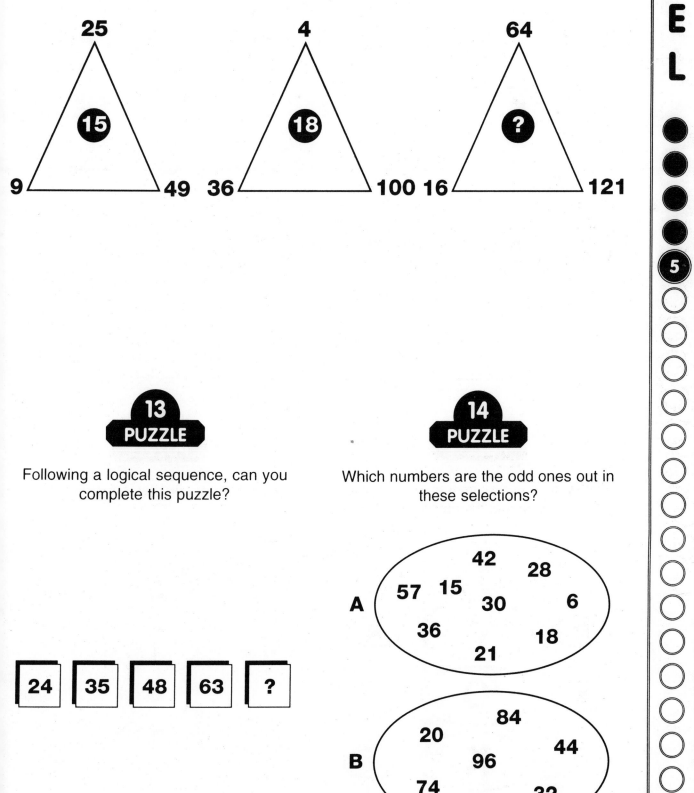

25

(15)

9   49

4

(18)

36   100

64

(?)

16   121

13 PUZZLE

Following a logical sequence, can you complete this puzzle?

| 24 | 35 | 48 | 63 | ? |

14 PUZZLE

Which numbers are the odd ones out in these selections?

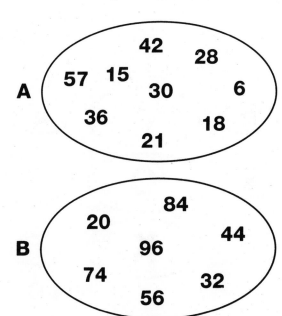

A

42   28
57   15
        30   6
36   18
    21

B

        84
20
            96   44
74
        56   32

L
E
V
E
L

5

PUZZLE 15

What completes this triangle of numbers?

(9)

(6) (3)

(5) (4)

(7) (2) (1) (?)

PUZZLE 16

What is missing from this puzzle?

〈19〉 〈14〉 〈17〉

〈11〉 〈9〉 〈15〉

〈8〉 〈5〉 〈?〉

PUZZLE 17

Following a logical sequence, can you complete this puzzle?

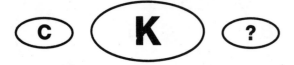

D	**J**	N
G	**O**	V
C	**K**	?

PUZZLE 18

Which letter completes the puzzle?

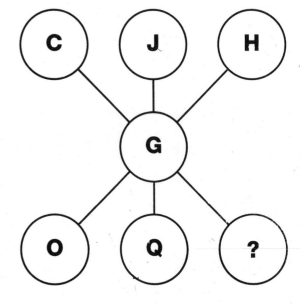

C   J   H

G

O   Q   ?

Which number completes this puzzle?

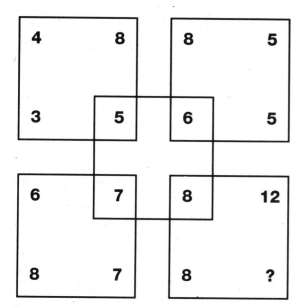

In this logical sequence of letters, what is needed to make it complete?

What is missing?

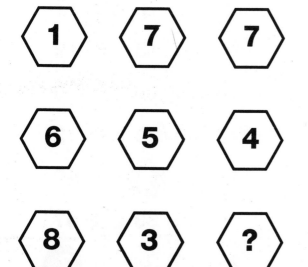

What number is missing?

LEVEL 5

LEVEL

5

Which number is missing?

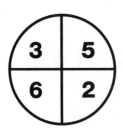 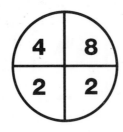

3	5
6	2

4	8
2	2

 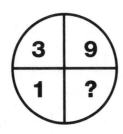

2	7
4	3

3	9
1	?

Which value replaces the question mark and balances the scale?

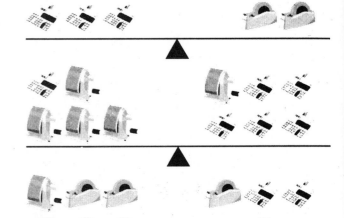

Which playing card completes the puzzle?

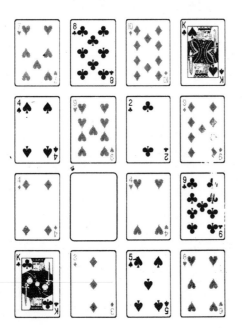

What three numbers are missing from this grid?

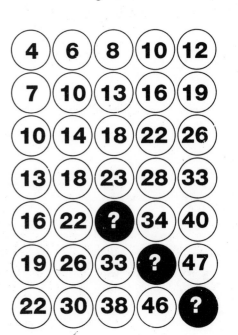

4	6	8	10	12
7	10	13	16	19
10	14	18	22	26
13	18	23	28	33
16	22	?	34	40
19	26	33	?	47
22	30	38	46	?

Which pattern completes this sequence?

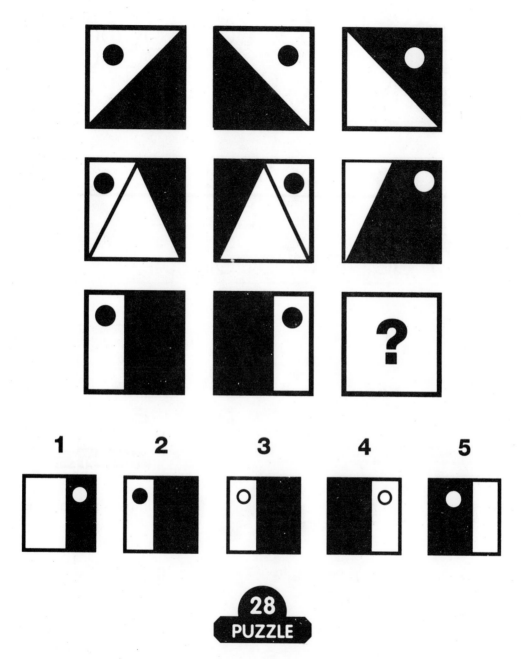

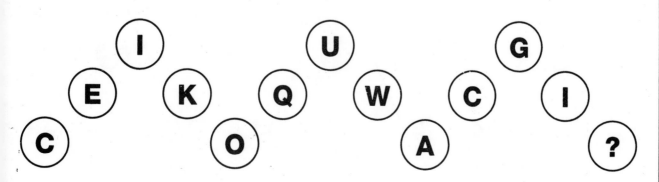

Following a logical sequence, can you complete this puzzle?

LEVEL

5

PUZZLE 1

Which of the lower six grids completes the sequence?

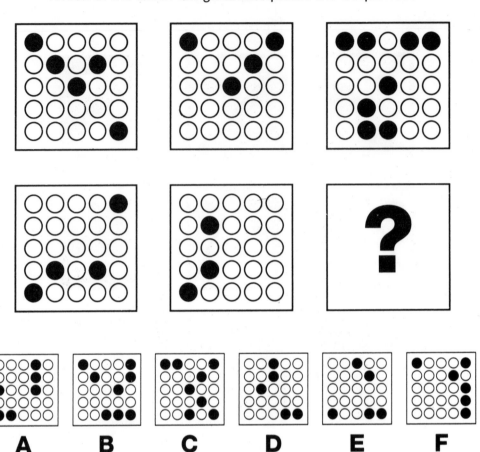

A   **B**   **C**   **D**   **E**   **F**

PUZZLE 2

What is missing from the last triangle?

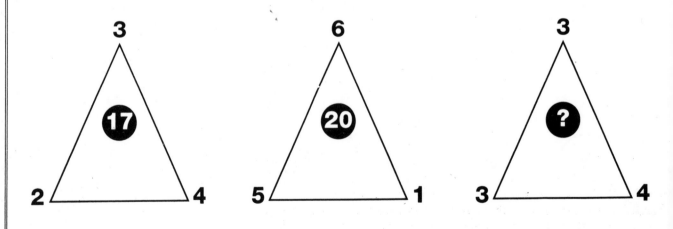

PUZZLE 3
What number is missing?

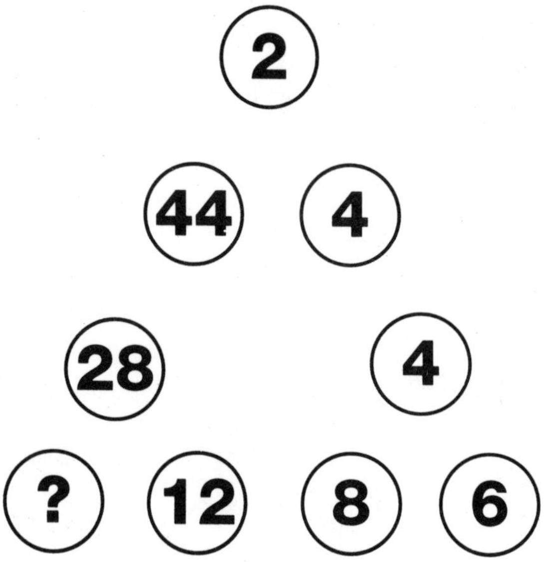

2

44   4

28   4

? 12 8 6

PUZZLE 4
Which number completes this sequence?

8	5	3
5	7	12
7	8	?

PUZZLE 5
Which letter completes the puzzle?

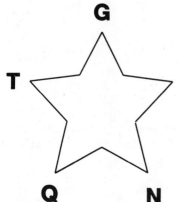
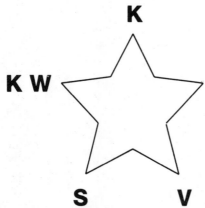
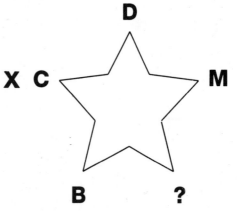

Star 1: G (top), T (left), K (right), Q (bottom-left), N (bottom-right)

Star 2: K (top), W (left), X (right), S (bottom-left), V (bottom-right)

Star 3: D (top), C (left), M (right), B (bottom-left), ? (bottom-right)

LEVEL

6

55

PUZZLE 6

Following a logical sequence, can you complete this puzzle?

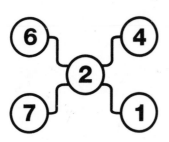 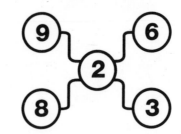 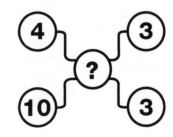

PUZZLE 7

What is missing from the last shape?

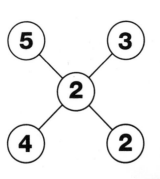 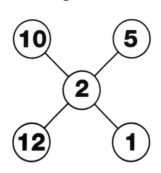 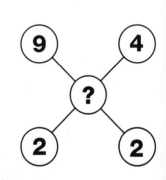

PUZZLE 8

Which number fits within the bottom right hand circle to complete the puzzle?

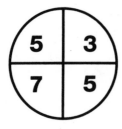 

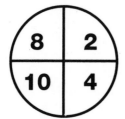 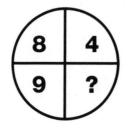

PUZZLE 9

Which letter completes the puzzle?

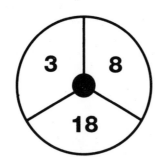

Which number is missing from the last circle?

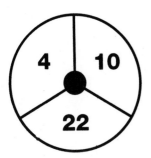

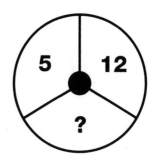

What number is missing?

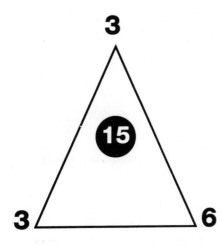

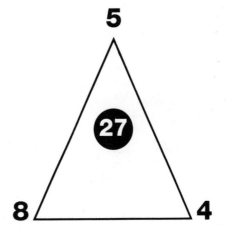

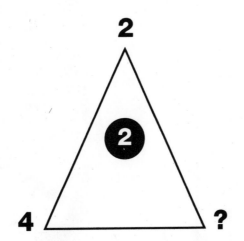

Which number completes this puzzle?

3	3	7
1	5	1
1	8	?

In this sequence of letters, what is need to complete the puzzle?

J	K
M	P
T	Y
E	L
T	C
M	?

What is needed to complete this pyramid of numbers?

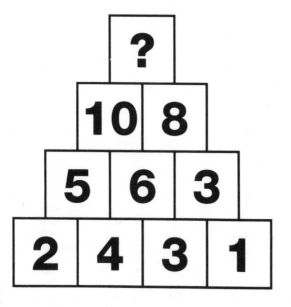

Which letter completes the puzzle?

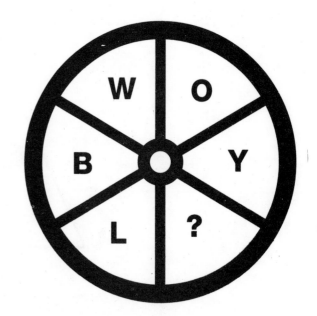

PUZZLE 16

Which letter goes within this triangle?

O

K   U

E   A

Y   S   M   ?

PUZZLE 17

What is missing from this sequence?

63

58

51

42

31

?

PUZZLE 18

Following a logical sequence, can you complete this puzzle?

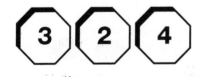

3   2   4

9   24

1   5   2

8   ?

PUZZLE 19

What letter is missing?

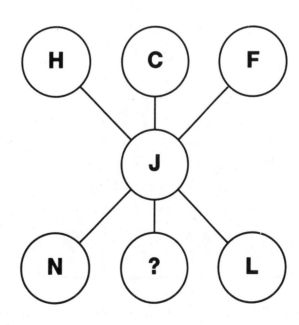

H   C   F

J

N   ?   L

LEVEL

6

59

PUZZLE 20

What is needed to complete this puzzle?

R

W

C

J

?

PUZZLE 21

Which letters complete the puzzle?

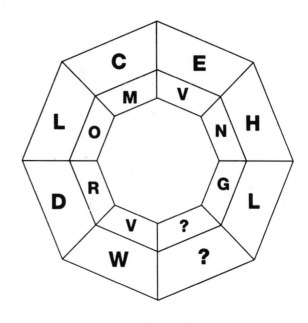

PUZZLE 22

What letter completes this pyramid?

PUZZLE 23

Can you move just 4 matches to make 3 equilateral triangles?

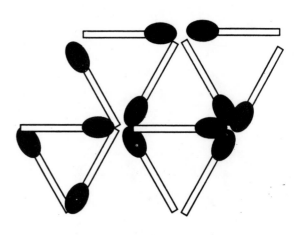

Which letter is the odd one out in each oval?

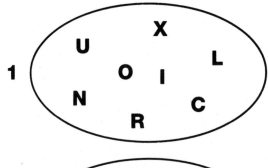

1

2

Where does the missing hand go?

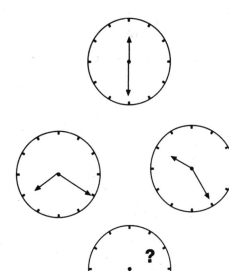

Following a logical sequence, can you complete this puzzle?

4 11 25 53 ?

What goes in the empty segment?

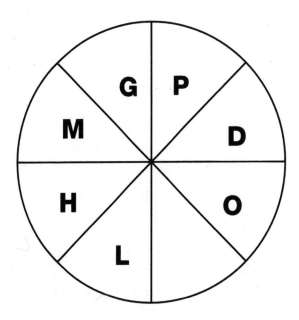

L E V E L

6

28 PUZZLE

What number is missing?

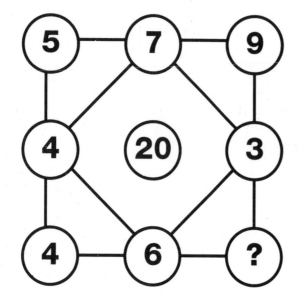

30 PUZZLE

What needs to be added to the third set of scales to make it balance perfectly?

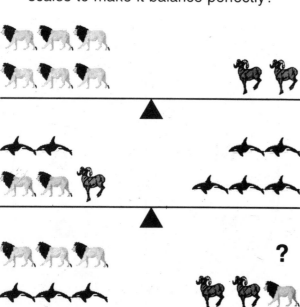

29 PUZZLE

Following a logical sequence, can you complete this puzzle?

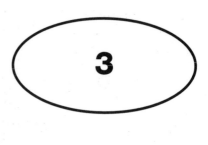

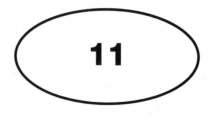

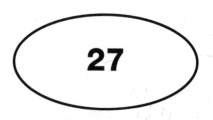

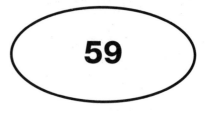

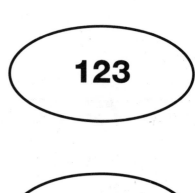

1 PUZZLE

What completes this puzzle?

G   N   Q

C

D   K   ?

2 PUZZLE

Which letter completes the puzzle?

N

V   Z

D   R

L   T   B   ?

3 PUZZLE

Which of the lower patterns replaces the question mark to continue the sequence?

 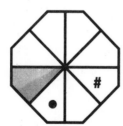  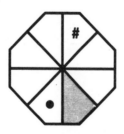 

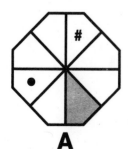 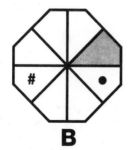 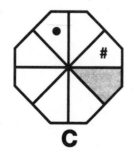 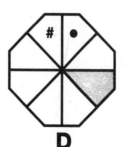 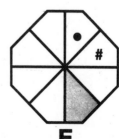

A   B   C   D   E

PUZZLE 4

What number is missing?

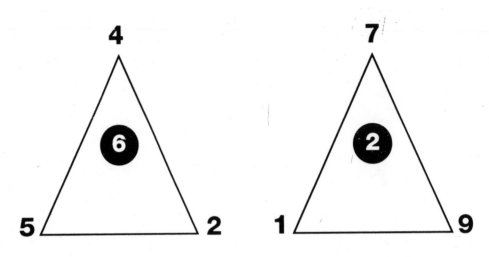

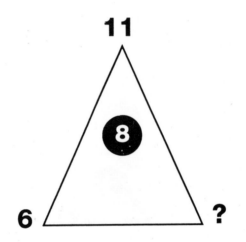

PUZZLE 5

What is missing from the last star?

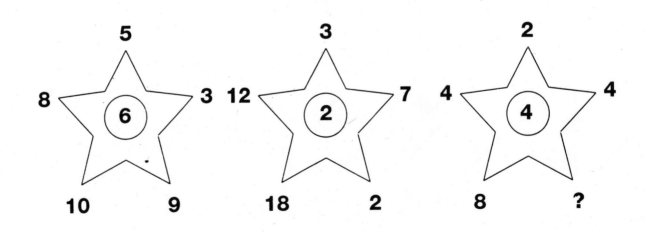

Which letter completes the puzzle?

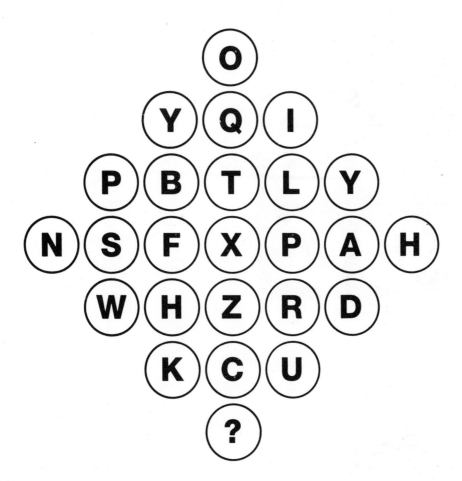

Following a logical sequence, can you complete this puzzle?

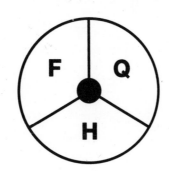
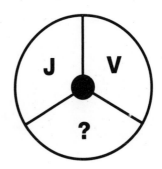

PUZZLE 8

Which number completes this puzzle?

PUZZLE 9

Where does the missing hand go?

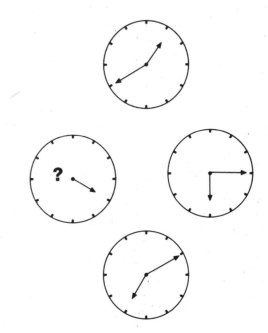

PUZZLE 10

Which letter follows? (Clue: this is the first time you have needed to think like this)

| B | C | D | G | ? |

PUZZLE 11

In this sequence of numbers, what completes the puzzle?

5	7
7	10
11	16
19	28
35	52
67	?

12 PUZZLE

What number is missing?

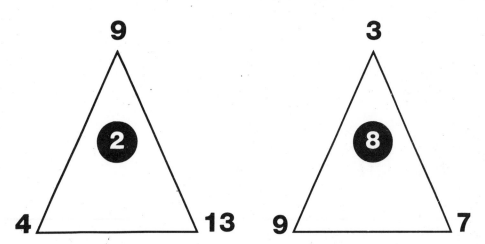

9
2
4   13

3
8
9   7

6
6
5   ?

13 PUZZLE

What is missing from the last triangle?

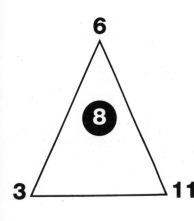

6
8
3   11

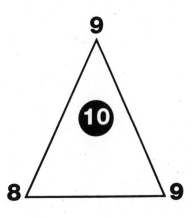

9
10
8   9

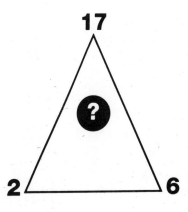

17
?
2   6

LEVEL

7

67

LEVEL

PUZZLE 14

What is needed in this triangle to complete the puzzle?

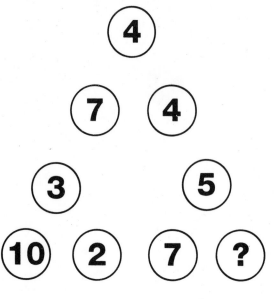

PUZZLE 15

Which letter completes the puzzle?

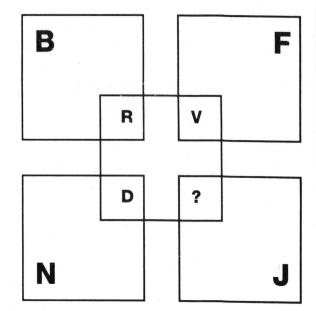

PUZZLE 16

Following a logical sequence, can you complete this puzzle?

92

74

46

22

?

PUZZLE 17

What letter is missing?

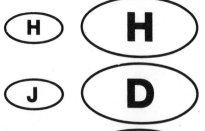

PUZZLE 18

Which number goes in the lower right hand segment?

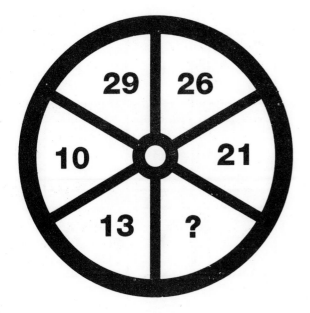

PUZZLE 19

What replaces the question mark?

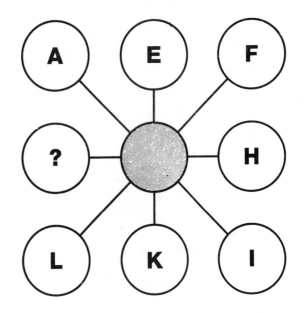

PUZZLE 20

Following a logical sequence, can you complete this puzzle?

PUZZLE 21

Can you remove three matches to leave three squares?

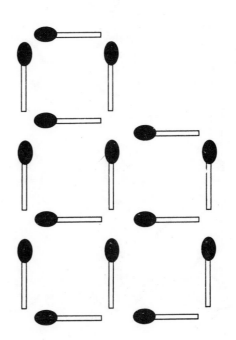

What completes this sequence?

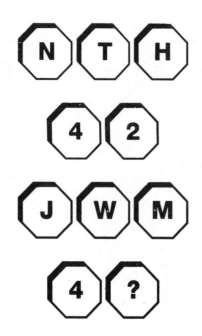

Which letter completes the puzzle?

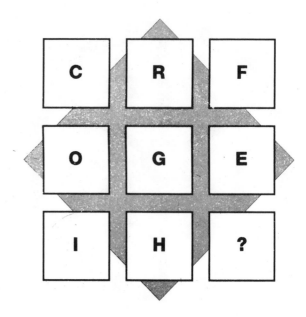

What number is missing?

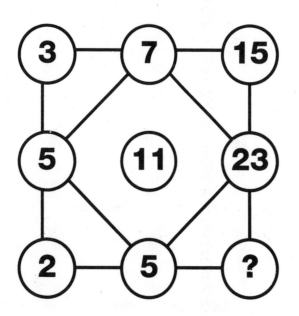

Can you trace around this figure using only 10 straight lines, without lifting your pen off the paper, or drawing over any line twice?

26 PUZZLE

Complete this puzzle.

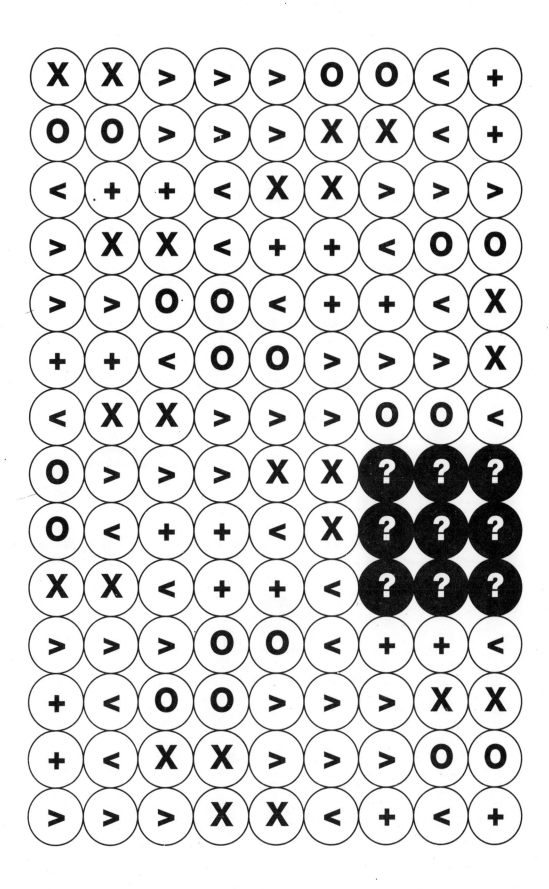

PUZZLE 1

Which letter completes the puzzle?

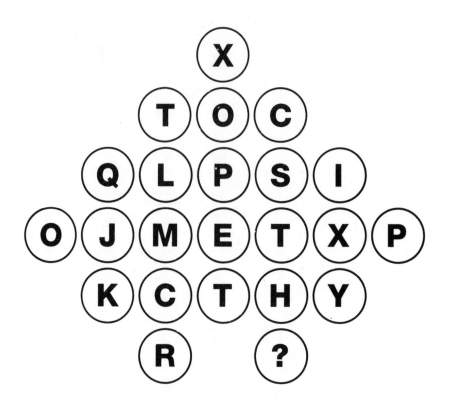

PUZZLE 2

Which number is missing?

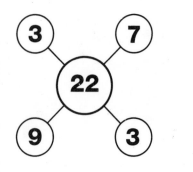

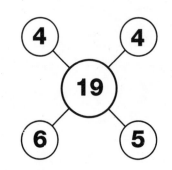

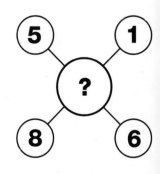

3
PUZZLE

What number is missing?

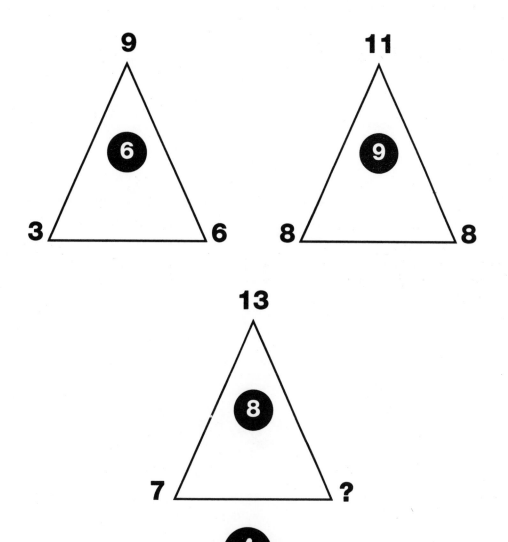

9

6

3   6

11

9

8   8

13

8

7   ?

4
PUZZLE

Which number replaces the question mark?

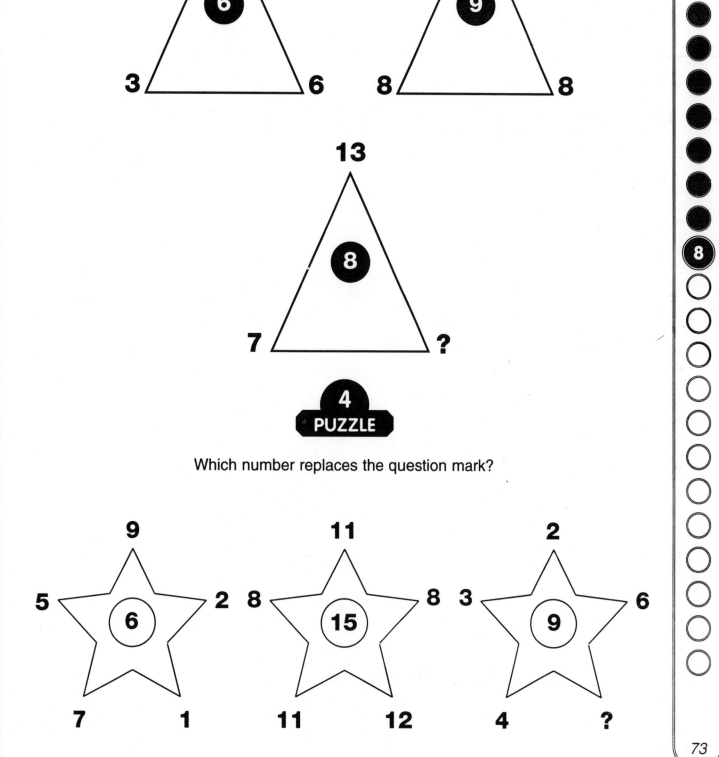

9

5   6   2

7   1

11

8   15   8

11   12

2

3   9   6

4   ?

L
E
V
E
L

8

73

5
PUZZLE

What is missing from the bottom square?

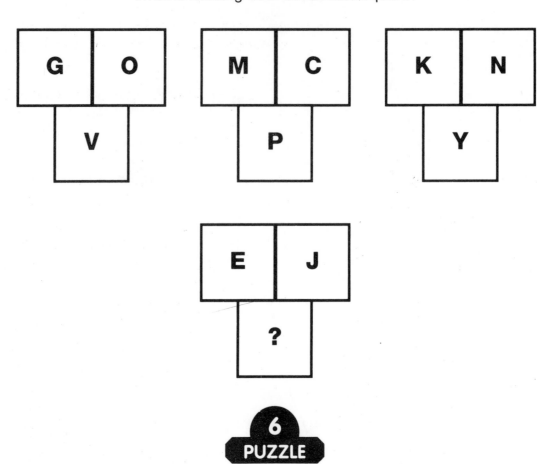

6
PUZZLE

Which of the bottom watches fills the empty space?

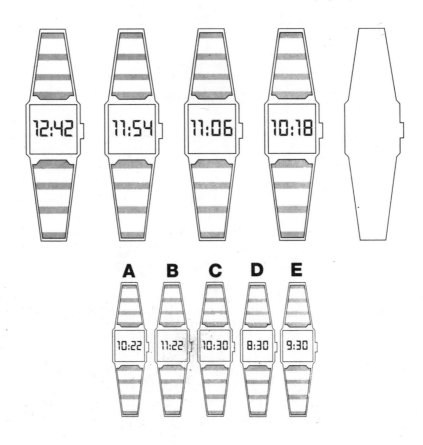

A 10:22 **B** 11:22 **C** 10:30 **D** 8:30 **E** 9:30

LEVEL

8

74

7
PUZZLE

Following a logical sequence, can you complete this puzzle?

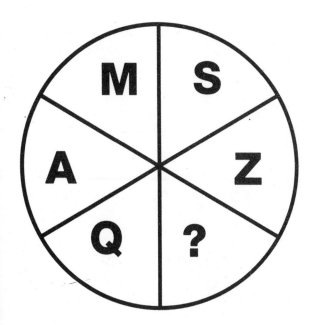

8
PUZZLE

What letter is missing?

9
PUZZLE

Which two letters complete this puzzle?

B	F	J	N	R	V	Z	D	H
M	R	W	B	G	L	Q	V	?
G	M	S	Y	E	K	Q	W	C
J	Q	X	E	L	S	Z	G	N
V	D	L	T	B	J	R	Z	?
Q	Z	I	R	A	J	S	B	K
V	F	P	Z	J	T	D	N	X

PUZZLE 10

What completes this puzzle?

5 6 3

9 11 5

17 21 ?

PUZZLE 11

Which letter is needed to complete the puzzle?

L	A	P
Q	F	U
V	K	?

PUZZLE 12

Which of the lower patterns finishes the sequence?

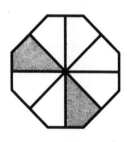 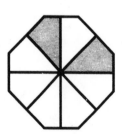 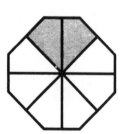 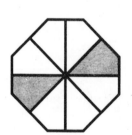 

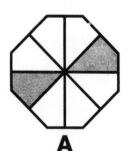    

A   B   C   D   E

What number is missing?

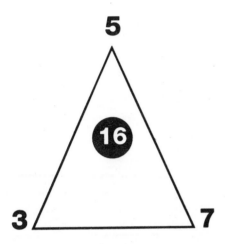

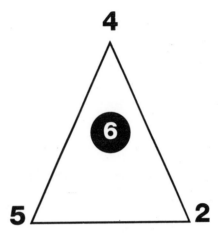

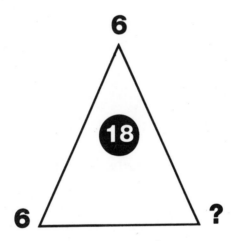

Following a logical sequence, can you complete this puzzle?

C   M   W   G   ?

What is needed to complete this sequence?

C
I
P
X
G
?

LEVEL

8

PUZZLE 16

What number is missing from the centre?

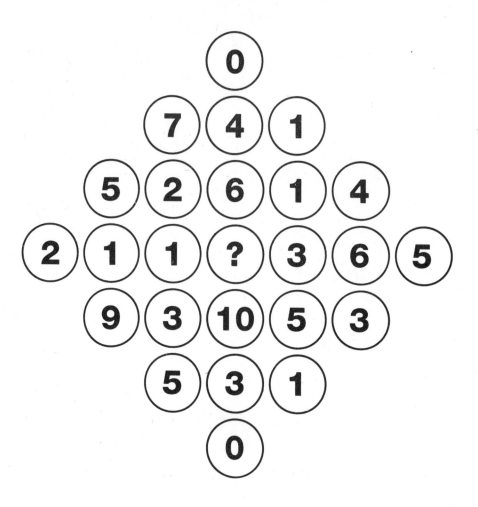

PUZZLE 17

Move two matches only to make this sum correct.

18 PUZZLE

Which letter is missing?

A

D

I

P

?

19 PUZZLE

Which number completes this wheel?

20 PUZZLE

Which number completes the puzzle?

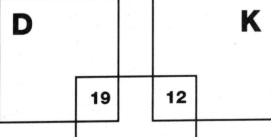
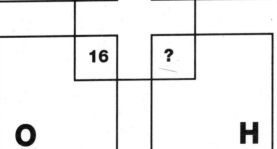

D

K

19

12

16

?

O

H

21 PUZZLE

What is needed to complete this sequence?

5	9
14	4
18	10
28	8
36	20
56	?

PUZZLE 22

Following a logical sequence, can you complete this puzzle?

PUZZLE 23

What number is missing?

PUZZLE 24

What number is missing from the bottom right hand circle?

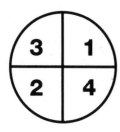
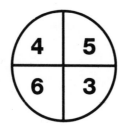

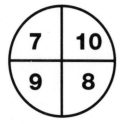
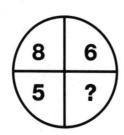

PUZZLE 25

Where should the missing hand go?

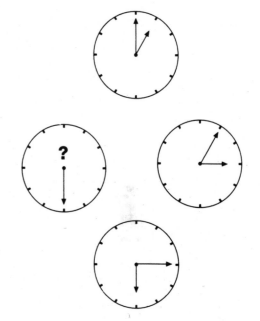

What is missing from this wheel?

Which letter completes the puzzle?

B   F   J   P   ?

What number is missing?

What is needed to complete this puzzle?

L
E
V
E
L

9

81

PUZZLE 5

What number is missing from the bottom triangle?

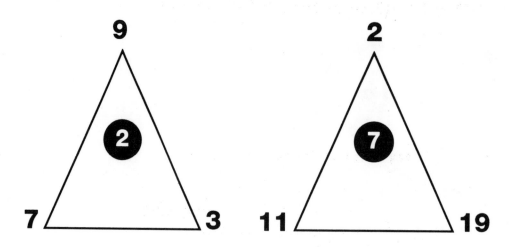

9

2

7   3

2

7

11   19

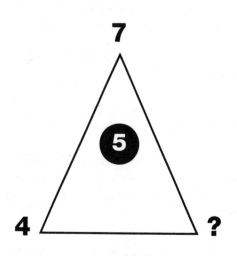

7

5

4   ?

PUZZLE 6

Which letter should go on top of the last star?

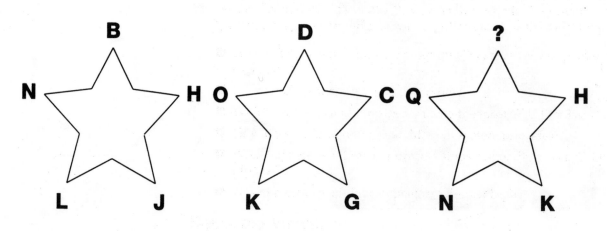

B
N   H
L   J

D
O   C
K   G

?
Q   H
N   K

PUZZLE 7

What completes this grid?

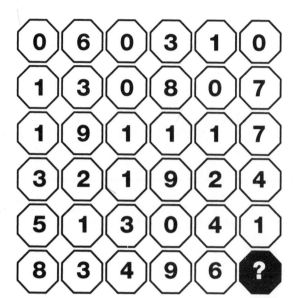

0	6	0	3	1	0
1	3	0	8	0	7
1	9	1	1	1	7
3	2	1	9	2	4
5	1	3	0	4	1
8	3	4	9	6	?

PUZZLE 8

Following a logical sequence, can you complete this puzzle?

5
7
11
19
?

PUZZLE 9

Which piece fits back into the grid?

5	3	6	8	1	1	7	4	7	0
9	2	1	3	7	8	3	6	3	8
1	3	0	6	4	6	1	0	5	9
6	4	5	3	■	■	2	3	4	7
4	7	9	■	■	■	1	6	4	
4	6	1	■	■	■	9	7	4	
7	4	3	2	■	■	3	5	4	6
9	5	0	1	6	4	6	0	3	1
8	3	6	3	8	7	3	1	2	9
0	7	4	7	1	1	8	6	3	5

1
```
  9 8
3 5 0 7
7 0 5 3
  8 9
```

2
```
    8 7
8 0 3 9
0 5 3 5
    9 7
```

3
```
  9 7
3 5 1 8
8 1 5 3
  7 9
```

4
```
  4 8
3 1 0 7
7 9 4 6
  2 7
```

5
```
  7 3
8 0 5 9
9 5 0 8
  3 7
```

Which of the bottom watches fills the gap?

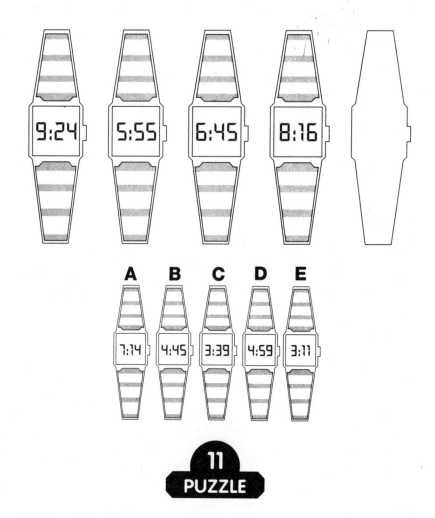

A   B   C   D   E

11 PUZZLE

Which of the bottom patterns replaces the question mark?

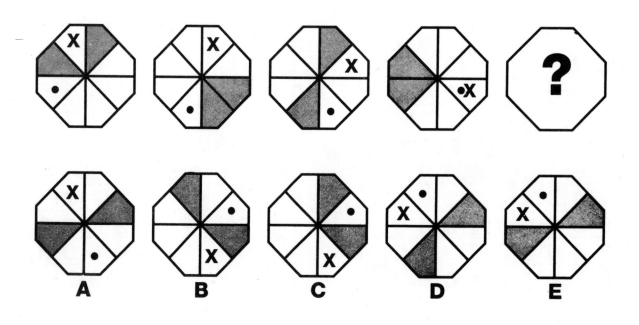

A   B   C   D   E

PUZZLE 12

Following a logical sequence, can you complete this puzzle?

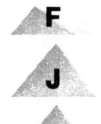

C

D

F

J

?

PUZZLE 13

What number is missing?

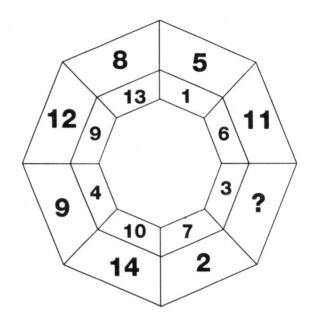

PUZZLE 14

What number completes the puzzle?

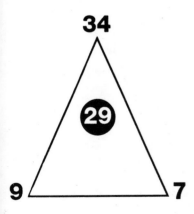

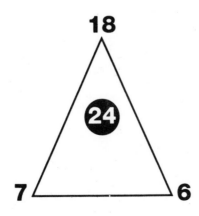

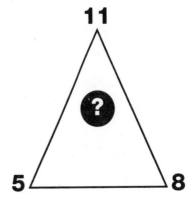

L E V E L

9

85

15
PUZZLE

What is needed to complete this grid?

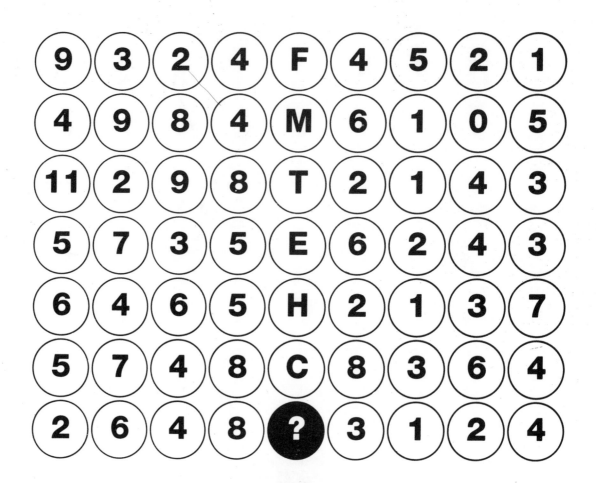

16
PUZZLE

Which number is missing from the last star?

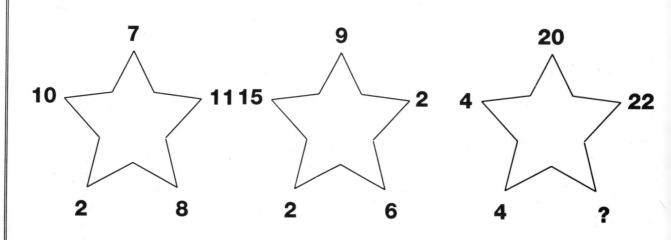

PUZZLE 17

Which letter is missing?

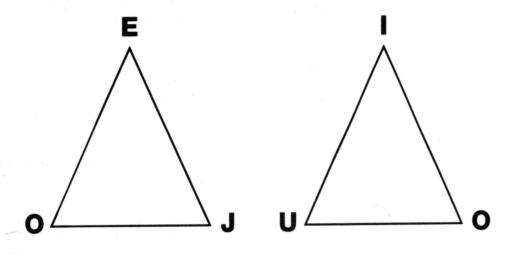

E
O — J
I
U — O

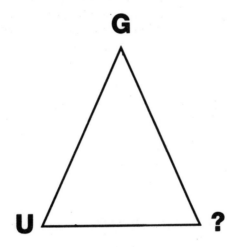

G
U — ?

PUZZLE 18

What number is missing?

2   9
3

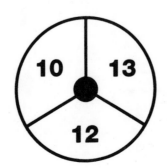

10   13
12

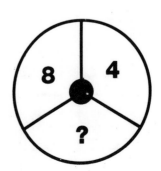

8   4
?

LEVEL

9

PUZZLE 19

What is missing from the last shape?

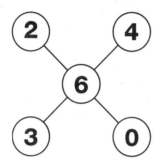

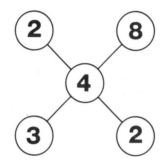

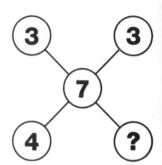

PUZZLE 20

Following a logical sequence, can you complete this puzzle?

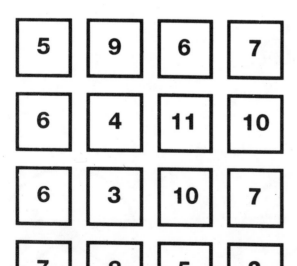

PUZZLE 21

Move just four matches to reduce the area of this triangle by exactly half.

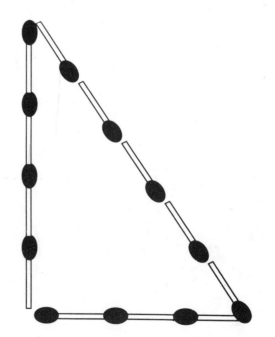

PUZZLE 22

What number is missing?

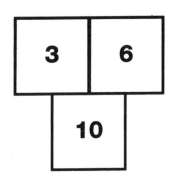

3 | 6
10

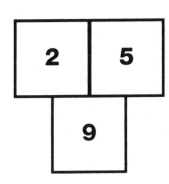

2 | 5
9

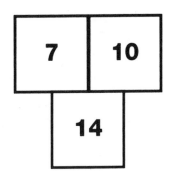

7 | 10
14

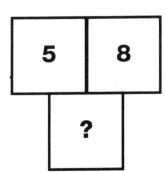

5 | 8
?

PUZZLE 23

Which letter completes the wheel?

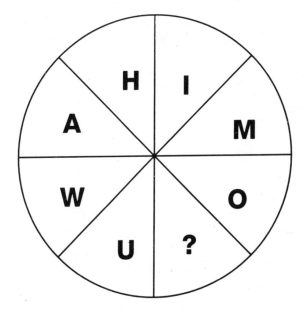

A H I M O U ? W

PUZZLE 24

Place every digit 1 to 9, in this puzzle, so that all horizontal, vertical and diagonal lines add up to the same number.

L
E
V
E
L

9

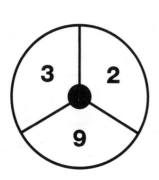

LEVEL

10

90

1 PUZZLE

Which letter completes the puzzle?

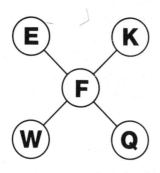

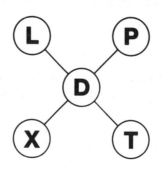

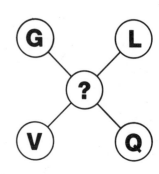

2 PUZZLE

Fill in the empty segment.

3 PUZZLE

What letter is missing?

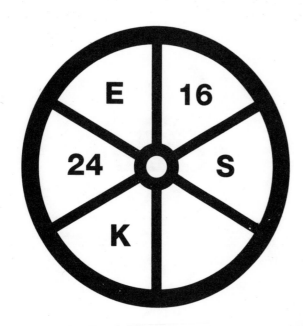

4 PUZZLE

What number is missing?

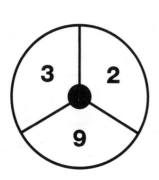

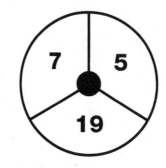

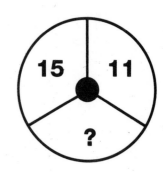

PUZZLE 5

What number goes in the centre of the bottom triangle?

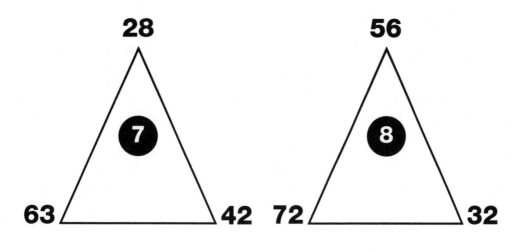

28
7
63   42

56
8
72   32

27
?
9   63

PUZZLE 6

Following a logical sequence, can you complete this puzzle?

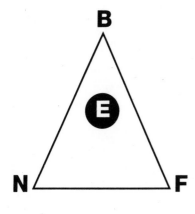

B
E
N   F

D
G
I   G

E
?
K   C

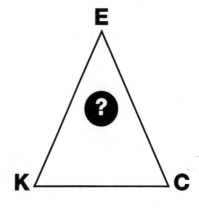

LEVEL

10

PUZZLE 7

Where does the missing hand go?

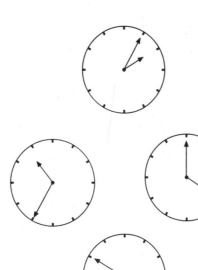

PUZZLE 8

Which letter completes the puzzle?

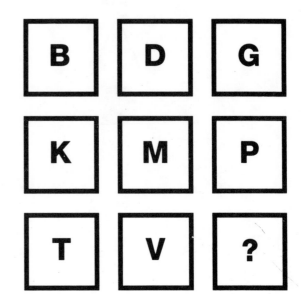

B	D	G
K	M	P
T	V	?

PUZZLE 9

What number is missing?

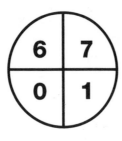

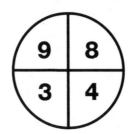

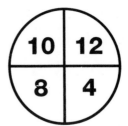

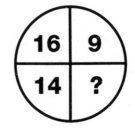

10 PUZZLE

Which letter completes the puzzle?

  11 PUZZLE

What number is missing?

H

X Q

M Y

A Q L ?

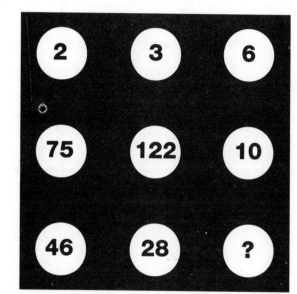

2 3 6
75 122 10
46 28 ?

L
E
V
E
L

10

12 PUZZLE

Which letter completes this puzzle?

G L E

C R O

K T ?

13 PUZZLE

Following a logical sequence, can you complete this puzzle?

13

17

19

23

?

14
PUZZLE

Which of the bottom watches completes the sequence?

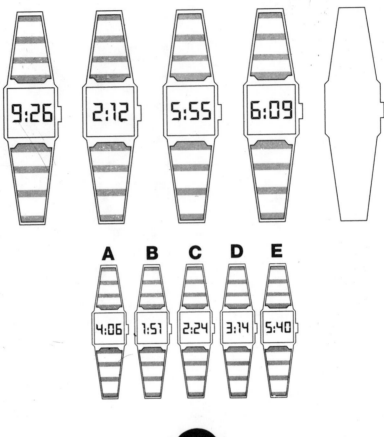

A   **B**   **C**   **D**   **E**

4:06   1:51   2:24   3:14   5:40

15
PUZZLE

What is missing from this puzzle?

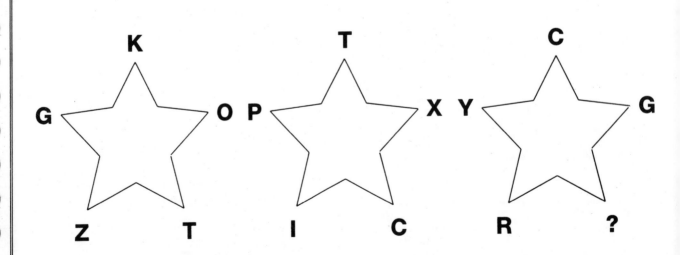

K

G   O

Z   T

T

P   X

I   C

C

Y   G

R   ?

Which letter completes this puzzle?

What is missing from this sequence of numbers?

What number is missing?

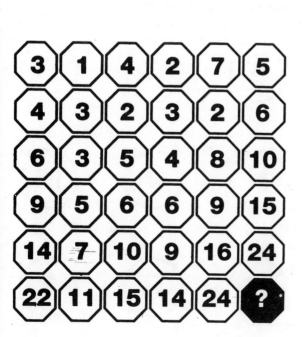

What completes this puzzle?

8	12	9
10	7	20
3	10	?

LEVEL

10

PUZZLE 20

What completes this pyramid?

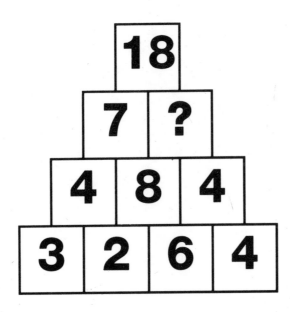

PUZZLE 21

What is missing from the wheel?

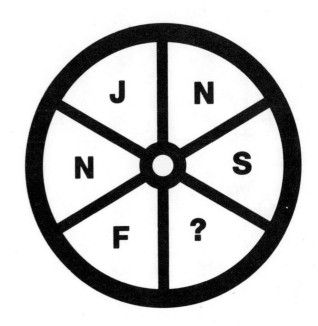

PUZZLE 22

What is missing from the empty segment?

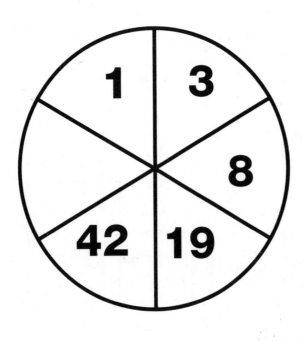

PUZZLE 23

What completes this puzzle?

Following a logical sequence, can you complete this puzzle?

Which three letters complete this puzzle?

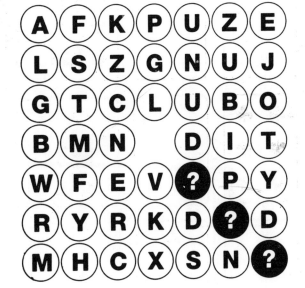

Can you draw 4 straight lines, which will pass through each of the dots on the diagram?

Can you fill in the blank boxes in the diagram, so that all horizontal, vertical and diagonal lines add up to 33?

LEVEL

10

Which playing cards fill in the missing gaps?

SOLUTIONS

1 - 7
Starting on the top row, and taking straight lines through the centre, subtract the central number from the upper number, and put the result in the corresponding lower box.

2 - 7
Working in rows, add the left and right hand numbers to give a 2 digit result, and write this in the middle two boxes.

3 - 9
In each row, the central number equals the average of the left and right hand numbers.

4 - G
In each row, multiply the numerical values of the left and right hand letters together to give the value in the centre.

5 - 8
In each triangle, divide the top number by the lower left number and add the lower right number to give the value in the centre of the triangle.

6 - 7
In each segment, the difference between the outer and inner numbers is always 9, with the highest and lowest numbers alternating from the inner ring to the outer ring each step

7 - 5
Working in rows, the central number equals the average of the left and right hand values.

8 - C
In each figure, letters move in sequence, clockwise, in steps given by the numerical value of the central letter.

9 - 25
Starting top left and moving clockwise, numbers increase by 6 each step.

10 - N
Working in rows from left to right, letters advance through the alphabet skipping 1 letter in the top row, 2 letters in the middle, and 3 for the bottom.

11 - 7
All rows and columns add up to 15.

12 - K
Starting at the top left, and working in a Z shape around the circles, letters follow the alphabetic sequence, skipping 1,2,3... etc., letters at a time.

13 - A
As you move to the right, add 24 minutes to each time value.

14 - G
In each shape, the numbers around the outside are all multiples of the number indicated by the numerical value of the letter in the centre.

15 - 9
Working in columns, from top to bottom, double each number and subtract 1 to give the next value down.

16 - 50
As you move to the right, double each number, and subtract 2.

17 - W
Starting on the left, letters advance by 3 places, then 4, 5 and 6.

18 - 28
As you descend, add 3 to the previous number, then 4, 5, 6... etc.

19 - 81
Starting at the top, numbers follow the sequence of square numbers of 5, 6, 7, 8 and 9.

20 - A
Starting on the left, and moving right, the 2 shaded segments rotate in opposite directions, 1 space at a time, while the dot moves one segment anticlockwise.

21 - F
Taking each grid of dots in the top row, rotate the pattern by 180° to form the pattern in the bottom row.

22 - Four of Diamonds
In each row, the sum of the black cards is always 7, the sum of the red cards is always 8. One card from each suit appears in each row.

23 - 2
Taking the horizontal line of circles through the centre of the diagram, these values equal the sum of the two adjacent numbers in the pattern.

24 - 1
Starting in the top left, and moving clockwise, the sum of the digits in each circle follows the the sequence 6, 7, 8 and 9.

25 - I
Starting in the top left, and moving clockwise in a spiral, towards the centre, letters move through the alphabet, skipping 1 letter at a time.

26 -

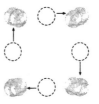

27 - 3
Add the top row of digits together, to give the result on the left hand centre space, and add the bottom row of digits together to give the result on the right hand centre space.

28 -

Working in columns, from top to bottom, the last circle represents the addition of the shaded segments from the top 3 circles. If a shaded segment appears in one of the top 3 circles, it appears in the same position in the bottom circle. If there are 2 shaded segments in the same position in the upper circles, then they cancel out, and become blank in the bottom circle. Shaded squares in all three remain shaded.

29 -

Reading from left to right, the sum of the dots on each domino follows the sequence 2, 4, 6, 8, 10, 12.

SOLUTIONS

LEVEL 2

1 - 7
Working in rows, from top to bottom, the sum of the digits in each row follows the sequence 10, 15, 20, 25, 30.

2 - F
All patterns of dots are symmetrical around a central vertical axis.

3 - Points to the 2 (6:10)
Starting at the top, and working clockwise around the faces, the time shown increases by 1 hour and 20 minutes each step.

4 - 2
In each circle, add the numbers in the top two segments together, to get a 2 digit number, and write this number in the lower two segments.

5 - H
Starting top left, and moving down, then up the centre, and down the right hand column, to finish bottom right, the letters follow the alphabetic sequence, 6 letters at time.

6 - 4
In each row, square the central number to give a 2 digit value, and write this value in the left and right hand spaces.

7 - S
Working clockwise around each shape, letters advance by steps of 3, 4 and 5, working from left to right.

8 - J
Letters in each position on the left triangle increase by steps of 4, 5, 6 and 7 as you move to the next triangle to the right, returning to the start of the alphabet once reaching Z.

9 - J
Working in columns, add the numerical values of the top two letters, to give the numerical value of the lower letter.

10 - 9
Starting with the numbers on the top row, add the central number to each one, giving the results on the bottom row.

11 - A
Starting with the letter C and moving clockwise, letters advance through the alphabet 5 letters at a time.

12 - 3
The sum of the digits on each side of the triangle equals 15.

13 - 62
Starting at the top, add 1 to the first number, and multiply by 2 to give the next number down.

14 - 2
Working in columns, the numbers in each column add up to 17.

15 - D
The sum of the digits shown on each watch increase by 2 each step.

16 - 5
Working in rows, from left to right, take the outer shape in each box and place it in the centre of the other shapes, moving 1 place to the right each time.

17 - 5
In each diagram, the numbers around the outside increase, in sequence, by value given in the central circle

18 - H
Starting top left and working down, then top right and down again, the letters follow the alphabetic sequence, 4 letters at a time.

19 - 40
Each horizontal row of numbers follows the sequence of multiples of 3, 4 and 5.

20 - 49
As you move to the right, the numbers follow the sequence of multiples of 7.

21 - 6
Reading the top line as a 3 digit number, subtract the central number, and write the 3 digit result in the lower circles.

22 - H
Starting at the apex of each triangle, and moving around it clockwise, letters skip 3 places for the left hand triangle, 4 places for the middle, and 5 places for the right hand triangle.

23 - Minute hand points to 4.
Starting with the top clockface, and moving clockwise around the other 3, the hour hand advances 3 hours at a time, and the minute hand moves back 20 minutes each time.

24 - X
Starting top left, and moving clockwise around the 4 circles, add 2 to the value of each letter to give the values of the letters in the next circle around.

25 - 78
Starting on the left, double each number, and add 2.

26 - M
Starting on A and moving clockwise, letters advance through the alphabet 3 at a time.

27 -

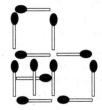

28 - 3
Add adjacent numbers on the bottom row, and put the results in the box directly above, take the difference between adjacent boxes on the next row up, putting the results in the box directly above again. Finally, take the sum of these two boxes, putting the result in the top box.

SOLUTIONS

1 - 10:25
Starting at the top, and moving clockwise around the faces, the minute hand moves forward by 10 minutes in each step, and the hour hand moves back one hour.

2 - Top O, P bottom R, Q
Starting in the top left, take 2X2 squares, with letters of the alphabet written in sequence clockwise, around these groups of 4. Work from left to right, top to bottom, writing the alphabet in sequence around the block.

3 - 3
Working from left to right, top row then bottom, the sum of the numbers in each circle increases by multiples of 5.

4 - 18
Starting at the top, and working down, add the first two numbers together, to give the next number down.

5 - 19
In each row of the diagram, the sum of the numbers is 19.

6 - 8
Working in columns, the number at the bottom of each row equals the difference between the upper two numbers.

7 - 1
In each row, the central number is equal to the sum of the right and left hand numbers.

8 - E
Each shape is rotationally symmetrical by 180° around its central point.

9 - 5
In each diagram, the average of the top two numbers, and the bottom two numbers is written in the central circle.

10 - 5
In each triangle, subtract the two lower numbers from the number at the top of the triangle to give the value at the centre.

11 - 63
Working in rows from left to right, and from top to bottom, numbers follow the sequence of multiples of 7, 8 and 9.

12 - 4
Working top to bottom, reading each pair of numbers as a two digit value, the values follow the sequence of square numbers, from 3 to 8.

13 - 26
Moving clockwise from number 5, numbers increase in value by 6,7,8,9 etc.

14 - 4
Working in rows, add the centre and right hand digits together, to give the result on the left.

15 - 3
Working in columns, the sum of the 3 numbers always equals 17.

16 - 5
Taking the top three circles, add together the lower two circles, to get the value in the upper circle, repeat this formula for the three circles on the bottom left and bottom right.

17 - 5
Starting with the numbers on the top row, and moving in straight lines through the centre, multiply the top numbers by the central number, putting the results in the lower circles.

18 - 4
In each row, the centre number equals the difference between the left and right hand numbers.

19 - 31
Starting on the bottom row, add adjacent numbers together to give the value in the box above them. Repeat up to the apex of the pyramid.

20 - 343
As you move to the right, the numbers follow the cube values of the numbers 3 to 7.

21 - C
Working in rows, superimpose the pattern of dots in the left and right hand grids, to form the middle grid.

22 - 57
Starting on the left, and working to the right, add 3 to the first number, then 6 to the next, repeat this sequence, alternately adding 3 then 6.

23 - From left to right Two of Diamonds, Five of Hearts, Ace of Hearts, Ace of Spades
Working in columns, the sum of the top three cards, and the sum of the lower three cards equals the value of the central card. Also, there are two cards of each suit in each row, apart from spades of which there is only one.

24 - 13
The boxes follow the sequence of prime numbers.

25 -

26 - 1: Q, 2: R
In the first oval, all the letters have even numerical values, and in the second, they are all odd.

27 - 24
Moving clockwise around the circle, numbers follow the sequence of multiples of 6.

SOLUTIONS

1 - M
In each segment, the sum of the numerical values of the outer and inner letters equals 26.

2 - 12
Working in rows, add 4 to the left hand digit to give the central value, and add 6 to this digit, to give the right hand value.

3 - E
Starting with the letter Q and moving clockwise, letters move backwards through the alphabet, in steps of 3, then 4, 5, 6 etc.

4 - 4
Working in columns, multiply the top and middle numbers together, and write the result in the lower box.

5 - D
Working from left to right, top row then bottom, the number of dots in each pattern increases by 1 each time, from 8 to 13.

6 - 4:47
Starting on the left, and moving right, add 1 to each digit and rotate their positions to the left.

7 - 1
Starting on the top row, and moving in straight lines through the central circle, values on the bottom row equal the difference between numbers on the top row and the central number.

8 - W
Starting at the top, and working down, add 5 and 3 alternating as you move down.

9 - J
Starting from B and moving clockwise, add the numerical values of the first two letters to give the value of the next letter around.

10 - K
Starting on the left, the numerical values of the letters follow the sequence of prime numbers.

11 - G
Starting with the left hand triangle, letters increase in steps of 2, 3 and 4, as you move to the right, with their positions moving 1 place clockwise around the points of the triangles.

12 - (From top to bottom) 5, 2, 3
Each row contains 4 two digit numbers, which follow the sequence of multiples of 4 for the top row, 5 for the next, then 6, 7, 8 and 9.

13 - 12
In each star, add up the digits at each point of the star, and divide by 3 to give the value at the centre.

14 - A
If you take the numerical values of each letter, all columns and rows add up to 15.

15 - T
Starting at the top, and working down through each row, left to right, letters follow the alphabetic sequence, in steps of 5.

16 - 5
In each diagram, the top left number minus the central number gives the top right number, and the bottom left added to the central number gives the bottom right.

17 - 25
In each circle, moving clockwise, double the first number and subtract 1 to give the next value.

18 - Q
In each star, letters move clockwise around the points skipping 1, 2, 3 and 4 letters each time.

19 - R
Working in columns, letters follow the alphabetic sequence, in steps of 3 for the left hand column, 4 for the middle and 5 for the right hand column.

20 -

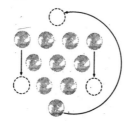

21 - 19
Starting top left, and moving in a Z shape around the circles, the numbers follow the sequence of prime numbers.

22 - A: 15, B: 4
In the first oval, all numbers are even, and in the second all numbers are odd.

23 - 16
Working clockwise, from 2, double each number to give the next one along.

24 - L
Working in rows, from left to right, letters are arranged in consecutive, alphabetical order.

25 - 5
Starting with the top left circle, and moving clockwise around the other 3, double each number and subtract 1 to give the values in the corresponding segments of the next circle around.

26 - Bananas

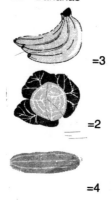

=3

=2

=4

27 -

Starting at the top, and moving clockwise, the minute hand moves back 25 minutes each time, while the hour hand moves forward 3 hours each time.

28 - A
Working in columns, the sum of the numerical values of the letters is written in the lower box.

29 - 2
Splitting the diagram vertically and horizontally, the same 5X5 pattern is displayed in each quarter.

SOLUTIONS

LEVEL 5

1 - 12
Working in columns, the sum of the top two numbers equals the value of the lower number.

2 - D
Starting in the top square, and working clockwise around it, letters advance through the alphabet, skipping 2 letters. Moving clockwise to the next square, the sequence of letters skips 3, then 4 etc.

3 - 11
Starting top left, and taking pairs of adjacent numbers, their total is always 20.

4 - O
Starting at the top left, and working in columns from left to right, letters follow the alphabetic sequence, skipping 4 letters at a time.

5 - Seven of Hearts
Working in columns, the sum of the left hand column equals 20, the next along totals 19, then 18, then 17. One card from each suit appears in each row.

6 - 6
In each diagram, multiply the top left number by the central one, to give the lower left number, and subtract the central number from the top right one to give the lower right number.

7 - 20
Starting at the top, add 7 to the first number to give the next one, then subtract 2 for the one after that, continue the same sequence for the remaining numbers.

8 - J
Starting in the top left, and moving clockwise in a spiral towards the centre, letters follow the alphabetic sequence, in steps of 8 letters.

9 - B
Working from left to right, add 1 to each digit and rotate from one place to the left.

10 - 2
In each circle, the sum of the segments always equals 13.

11 - A
Working in rows, from left to right, the number of dots in each pattern increases by 2 each time.

12 - 23
In each triangle, the value at the centre equals the sum of the square roots of the three numbers at each corner.

13 - 80
As you move right, numbers show the sequence of square numbers, from 5 to 9, subtracting 1 each time.

14 - A: Odd = 28, B: Odd = 74
In the first oval, all numbers are multiples of 3, and in the second, all numbers are a multiple of 4.

15 - 5
The value in each corner circle equals the sum of the values in the two adjacent circles.

16 - 2
Working in columns, the top number equals the sum of the lower two numbers.

17 - N
Working in rows, add the numerical values of the left hand and central letters, to give the value of the right hand letter.

18 - J
Starting with the letters on the top row, and moving in straight lines through the centre, add the numerical values of the top and central letters to give the value of the letters on the bottom row.

19 - 4
In each square, the average of the three outer numbers is written in the centre square.

20 - D
Working in columns, the sum of the numerical values of the letters in each column equals 22.

21 - 4
All columns and rows add up to 15.

22 - 43
The numbers increase by 7 each step.

23 - 3
In each circle, the sum of the 4 numbers equals 16.

24 - Pencil sharpener

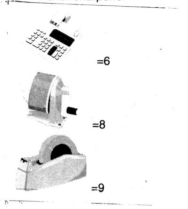

=6

=8

=9

25 - Jack of Spades
Starting at the top left, and working in rows, top to bottom, cards follow sequence, in steps of 1, 2, 3 etc., until 8, then 7, 6, 5 etc., There is 1 card of each suit in each line.

26 - Left to right, 28, 40, 54
In each row, numbers increase by 2, then 3, 4, 5 etc., as you go down.

27 - 1
Working in rows, starting on the left, reflect the first box around the vertical axis, to give the central box, and invert the colours of this box, to give the one on the right.

28 - M
Working from left to right, add 2 to the value of the first letter to give the next, add 4 to get the one after that, repeat this sequence, alternately adding 2 then 4.

SOLUTIONS

LEVEL 6

1 - E
If you superimpose the top row of grids onto the corresponding grids in the bottom row, the resulting pattern of dots form the letters X, Y and Z.

2 - 22
Square the two numbers at the bottom of each triangle, add them together and subtract the number at the top, to give the value in the middle of the triangle.

3 - 18
Starting at the top and moving clockwise, add the first two numbers together, and subtract 2, to give the next number in the sequence.

4 - 1
In each row, the sum of the odd numbers equals the even number.

5 - H
Taking pairs of letters from corresponding positions on the left and right hand stars, add their numerical values together, and put the result in the central star.

6 - 8
In each diagram, the difference between the sum of the odd numbers and the sum of the even numbers is written in the central circle.

7 - 9
In each diagram, the number in the centre equals the difference between the sum of the upper and lower pair of numbers.

8 - 5
In each circle, numbers in opposite segments add up to the same value 10 for top left, 11 for top right, 12 for bottom left and 13 for bottom right.

9 - S
Working in columns, add the numerical values of the top two letters together to give the value of the lower letter.

10 - 26
In each circle, multiply the lowest number by two, and add two, to give the next number.

11 - 1
In each triangle, multiply the bottom two numbers, and subtract the top number, to give the result in the centre of the triangle.

12 - 6
Reading each row as a 3 figure number, the top row minus the middle row equals the bottom row.

13 - X
Working top to bottom, left to right, letters follow the alphabetic sequence, skipping 1 letter, 2 letters, 3, 4, 5 etc.

14 - 17
Values in each box equal the sum of the two numbers in the boxes directly underneath, minus 1.

15 - D
Taking pairs of letters in opposite segments, one is the same distance from the start of the alphabet as the other is from the end.

16 - G
Starting at the apex of the triangle, and moving clockwise, letters advance through the alphabet 6 at a time.

17 - 18
Working from top to bottom, subtract 5 from the first number to give the next one down, then subtract 7, 9, 11 and 13 to give the rest.

18 - 10
Starting with the top two rows, add the numbers on the top together to give the lower left value, and multiply them together to give the lower right value. Repeat this sequence for the third and fourth row.

19 - Q
Letters on opposite sides of the central circle are the same number of letters away from the letter given in the central circle.

20 - R
Starting at the top, letters advance through the alphabet, in steps of 5, 6, 7 and 8.

21 - A, Q
In the outer circle, starting at C and moving clockwise, letters advance through the alphabet in steps of 2, 3, 4 etc. In the inner circle, starting at M and moving anti-clockwise, letters also advance through the alphabet in steps of 2, 3, 4 etc.

22 - K
Starting bottom left, and moving to alternate squares clockwise around the triangle, letters advance in steps of 3.

23 -

24 - 1: N, 2: O
In the first oval, the numerical values of the letters are all multiples of 3, and in the second, they are all multiples of 4.

25 -

In each clockface, the hour hand points to the number which is double the minute hand's number.

26 - 109
Working from left to right, multiply each number by two, and add 3 to get the next number along.

27 - E
Divide the circle, horizontally and vertically, into quarters. The numerical values of letters in adjacent segments in each quarter of the circle add up to 20.

28 - 2
The four numbers at the corners of the diagram, and the four numbers at the centre of each side, add up to 20.

29 - 251
Starting at the top, and working down, double each number and add 5 to give the next value down.

30 - Lion
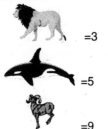

=3
=5
=9

104

SOLUTIONS

1 - N
Starting with the letters in the top row, subtract the numerical value of the central letter to give the letters on the bottom row.

2 - J
Starting at the top and moving anti-clockwise letters advance through the alphabet, 8 letters at a time.

3 - D
Starting on the left, and moving to the right, the dot moves from one segment to the one directly opposite, and back again. The # moves 1 place anticlockwise each time, as does the shaded segment.

4 - 11
The value of the numbers in the lower triangle equals the sum of the numbers, in corresponding positions on the upper two triangles.

5 - 7
Find the difference between corresponding pairs of numbers, on the left and central stars, and put the result in the same position on the right hand star.

6 - G
Starting on the left, and working down in columns, if possible, and moving to the right, letters follow alphabetic sequence, in steps of 2, 3 and 4, 2, 3 and 4 etc.

7 - N
Starting on the left, and moving to the corresponding segment on the right, letters increase in value by steps of 4, 5 and 6.

8 - 89
Starting top left and working down, then up the central column and down the right hand column, add the first two numbers together, to give the next along.

9 -

On each clockface, the numbers pointed to by the hour and minute hands add up to 9.

10 - J
Starting on the left, the letters follow the alphabetic sequence, skipping letters written with only straight lines.

11 - 100
For the left hand column, double each number, and subtract 3 to give the next number down, for the right hand column, double each number and subtract 4 to give the next number down.

12 - 6
Values on the lower triangle equal the difference between corresponding numbers on the upper two triangles.

13 - 9
In each triangle, the value in the centre equals the sum of the odd numbers around the points of the triangle, minus the sum of the even numbers.

14 - 3
Splitting the diagram into 3 smaller triangles one at the top and two at left and right, each containing 3 numbers, the sum of the number is always 15.

15 - Z
Starting top left, and moving clockwise around the outer squares, and then the inner squares, letters advance through the alphabet, skipping 3 letters at a time.

16 - 18
Starting at the top, multiply the two digits of each number together and subtract this total, to give the next value down.

17 - E
In each row the sum of the numerical values of each letter is always 20.

18 - 18
Starting top left, and moving clockwise, subtract 3 from an odd number to give the next value, and subtract 5 from an even number in the same way.

19 - M
Starting top left, and moving clockwise around the diagram. letters follow the alphabetic sequence, skipping any letters written with curved lines.

20 - 10
Working from top to bottom, add the first two numbers together, and subtract 3 to give the next value down.

21 -

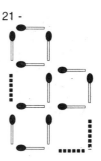

22 - 6
Add the numerical values of the letters in each row together, and put this 2 digit value in the line underneath.

23 - J
In each row, add numerical values of the left and right hand letters, and write the letter with the reverse alphabetical value in the centre square.

24 - 11
Working in rows, from left to right, multiply each number by 2 and add 1 to give the next number along.

25 -

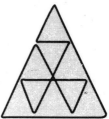

26 -   <   +   +
       X   >   >
       0   0   >
Start in the top left, and move in rows to the right, then down a row and to the left etc. in a snakes and ladders pattern, using the repeated sequence of symbols:
X X > > > 0 0 < + + <.

SOLUTIONS

1 - W
Follow lines of letters, from the middle left, diagonally up to the right, then diagonally down to the right etc, letters follow the alphabetic sequence, in steps of 2, 3, 4 etc.

2 - 20
In each diagram, the central number equals the sum of the four surrounding numbers.

3 - 4
In each triangle, the central number equals the average of the 3 surrounding numbers.

4 - 11
Time decreases by 48 minutes each step.

5 - O
In each set of 3 boxes, the sum of the numerical values of top two letters equals the numerical value of the lower letter.

6 - E
As you move to the right, subtract 1 from the hour value, and add 12 to the minute value. If the minutes exceeds 60, the hour value increases by 1.

7 - H
Starting top left, and moving clockwise, letters move forward by 6 places, then 7, 8, 9 etc.

8 - H
In each row, add the numerical values of the left and right hand letters, to give the reverse alphabetical value of the central letter.

9 - (top to bottom) A, H
Working in rows, from left to right, letters move through the alphabet in steps of 4 for the top row, 5 for the next, then 6, 7, 8 etc.

10 - 9
Working in columns, starting at the top, double each number and subtract 1 to give the next number down.

11 - Z
Starting top left, and working in columns, from left to right, letters move through the alphabet 5 places at a time.

12 - D
Working from left to right, one shaded section moves 1 segment clockwise at each turn, while the other moves two segments anticlockwise at each turn.

13 - 4
In each triangle, multiply the lower two numbers together, and subtract the top number, to give the result in the middle.

14 - Q
Starting on the left, letters advance 10 places in the alphabet as you move to the right, returning to the start of the alphabet after reaching Z.

15 - Q
Starting at the top, add 6 to the numerical value of the top letter to give the value of the next one down. Then 7, 8, 9 etc for the rest.

16 - 9
Working in rows, the central value equals half the sum of the other digits in each row.

17 -

18 - Y
Starting at the top and working down, the numerical value of each letter follows the sequence of square numbers, from 1 to 5.

19 - 159
Starting top left and moving clockwise, double each number and add 1 to give the next number round.

20 - 23
The reverse numerical value of each letter is written in the inner square is on the opposite side.

21 - 16
Starting from the top, add the left and right hand numbers together, to give the lower left hand number, and calculate their difference to give the lower right hand number.

22 - 35
Starting on the left, double each number, and subtract 3, to give the next number along.

23 - 13
Starting bottom left, and working clockwise, in a spiral, numbers increase by 5, then decrease by 2 alternately.

24 - 7
Starting in the top left circle and moving clockwise add 2 to each number, and rotate their positions 90° clockwise to give the values in the next circle.

25 -

Starting with the top clockface, and moving clockwise around the others, the minute hand moves forward by 1 division, then 2, then 3, while the hour hand moves forward by 2 divisions, then 3, then 4.

SOLUTIONS

LEVEL 9

1 - 1
Starting with each odd number, multiply by 2 and add 4 to give the number in the opposite segment.

2 - V
Working from left to right, letters represent the vowels in the alphabet, displaced 1 letter forward.

3 - 2
In each row, multiply the left and right hand numbers together, and subtract 5 to give the central number.

4 - U
Starting at the top left and working in rows, left to right, the letters follow the alphabetic sequence skipping 1 letter, then 2 letters, then 3, 4 etc.

5 - 16
Using pairs of numbers in corresponding positions on the upper two triangles, calculate their difference, and put the result in the corresponding position on the lower triangle.

6 - C
In each diagram, starting with the right hand point, and working clockwise, letters advance through the alphabet in steps given by the numerical value of the top letter.

7 - 5
Split the diagram twice, along a vertical axis, to give three columns, two spaces wide. Starting at the top of each column, reading each row as 2 digit numbers, add the top two numbers together to give the next 2 digit number down. continue this pattern for each column.

8 - 35
Working from top to bottom, multiply each number by 2 and subtract 3 to give the next value down.

9 - 5
Split the diagram into quarters, of 5X5 squares. There is a random pattern of numbers in the top left square, which is rotated 90° anticlockwise around the other three quarters.

10 - C
On each watch face, the digits add up to 15.

11 - C
Working from left to right, the X moves clockwise, one segment at a time, while the • moves anticlockwise. One shaded segment moves two spaces clockwise each time, while the other moves three spaces anticlockwise.

12 - R
Working from top to bottom, double the numerical value of each letter, and subtract two, to give the next letter down.

13 - 6
The sum of each outer number and the inner number of the opposite segment is always 15.

14 - 29
In each triangle, multiply the lower two numbers and subtract the number at the top, to give the value at the centre.

15 - J
In each row, the difference between the sum of the left hand numbers and the sum of the right hand numbers equals the numerical value of the letter in the centre.

16 - 6
In each star, add the top 3 numbers together to give a 2 digit number, and write these two digits on the lower points of the star.

17 - N
The difference between the numerical values of the bottom letters is written at the top of each triangle.

18 - 9
The numbers in the segments in the central circle equal the sum of the numbers in corresponding segments of the left and right hand circles.

19 - 0
In each diagram, reading the top and bottom pair of numbers as two digit values the centre number is the difference between them.

20 - 4
Working in columns, the sum of the even numbers equals the sum of the odd numbers.

21 -

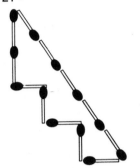

22 - 12
In each shape, starting top left and moving clockwise, numbers increase by 3, then 4.

23 - R
Moving clockwise around the circle, in alternate segments, one group of segments follows the alphabet in steps of 5, the other group in steps of 6.

24 -	8	3	4
	1	5	9
	6	7	2.

SOLUTIONS

1 - E
In each diagram starting at the top left and moving clockwise, letters follow the alphabetic sequence, skipping the number of letters each time, as indicated by the numerical number of the central letter.

2 - 10
Take the numerical value of each letter, and add 5 to give the numerical number in the opposite segment.

3 - L
Working in rows, the sum of the numerical values of the left and centre letters equals the numerical value of the right hand letter.

4 - 39
Starting on the left, double the value in each segment; and add 1 to give the values in the circle to the right.

5 - 3
In each triangle, the number in the centre is a common denominator for the three surrounding numbers.

6 - H
In each triangle, add up the numerical values of the letters around the outside, to give the reverse numerical value of the letter at the centre.

7 -

Starting at the top, and working clockwise around the faces, the minute hand moves back 5, 10 then 15 minutes, while the hour hand moves forward 2 hours then 3 then 4.

8 - Y
Starting at top left, and working in rows to the right, top to bottom, the letters follow the alphabetic sequence, skipping 1, 2 then 3 letters before repeating the sequence.

9 - 15
Working from left to right, top row then bottom, the sum of the two digits in the left hand segments of the circles follow the sequence of multiples of 6, and the sum of the right hand segments follow multiples of 4, starting at 8.

10 - F
Starting with A in the bottom left, and moving clockwise around the triangle letters follow the alphabetic sequence, jumping 12 letters, then 11, 10, 9 ..etc.

11 - 17
Starting top left, and moving clockwise in a spiral, towards the centre, add the first two numbers together, then add 1 to give the next number in the sequence.

12 - I
Working in rows, the numerical value of the central letter equals the sum of the numerical values of the left and right hand letters.

13 - 29
Working top to bottom, numbers follow the sequence of prime numbers.

14 - B
If the watch is viewed upside down, the digits appear to be the same.

15 - L
In each star, starting with the top letter and moving clockwise, letters increase in value by 4, 5, 6 and 7.

16 - B
Starting with the outer ring, add 5 to the numerical value of each letter and put the result in the inner segment, 1 place clockwise from the starting letter.

17 - 35
Working from top to bottom, double each number and subtract 3.

18 - 38
Starting top left, and working down in columns from left to right, add the first two numbers together and subtract 1 to give the next value down.

19 - 4
Working in columns, the sum of the even numbers, minus the odd number always equals 15.

20 - 10
Starting on the bottom row, the sum of the numbers in each row increases by 1 each time, from 15.

21 - Y
Starting with J, and moving clockwise, letters move through the alphabet in steps of 4, 5, 6 etc.

22 - 89
Starting with 1 and moving clockwise, double each number, and add 1, 2, 3 etc.

23 - U
Working in rows, from left to right, letters follow the alphabetic sequence, skipping 1 letter, then 2 letters.

24 - N
Starting in the top left segment of the top left circle, move clockwise around the segments, before moving onto the next circle clockwise, letters move through the alphabet in steps of 2, 3, 4, 5 etc.

25 - M, W, I
Starting at top left, move clockwise around the outer circles. letters follow the alphabetical sequence in steps of 5. Moving to the next set of circles in, the letters are in steps of 7, and the final central circles, in steps of 9.

26 -

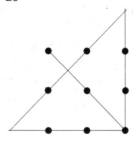

27 -

17	1	15
9	11	13
7	21	5

28 - Nine of Hearts, Seven of Spades, Nine of Diamonds
Starting top left, and moving clockwise in a spiral towards the centre, cards increase in value by 3 each time. The suits of the cards follow a repeated pattern, moving in an anti-clockwise spiral of hearts, clubs, diamonds, spades / spades, diamonds, clubs, hearts.